IMPROVING VOCABULARY SKILLS *SHORT VERSION*

D1308868

Sherrie L. Nist
UNIVERSITY OF GEORGIA

Carole Mohr

TOWNSEND PRESS   Marlton, NJ 08053

Books in the Townsend Press Reading Series:

GROUNDWORK FOR COLLEGE READING
GROUNDWORK FOR COLLEGE READING II
KEYS TO BETTER COLLEGE READING
TEN STEPS TO BUILDING COLLEGE READING SKILLS, 2/e
TEN STEPS TO IMPROVING COLLEGE READING SKILLS, 2/e
IMPROVING READING COMPREHENSION SKILLS
TEN STEPS TO ADVANCING COLLEGE READING SKILLS, 2/e

Books in the Townsend Press Vocabulary Series:

GROUNDWORK FOR A BETTER VOCABULARY
BUILDING VOCABULARY SKILLS
IMPROVING VOCABULARY SKILLS
ADVANCING VOCABULARY SKILLS
BUILDING VOCABULARY SKILLS, SHORT VERSION
IMPROVING VOCABULARY SKILLS, SHORT VERSION
ADVANCING VOCABULARY SKILLS, SHORT VERSION

Books in the Townsend Press Writing Series:

BASIC ENGLISH BRUSHUP, SHORT VERSION
ENGLISH BRUSHUP
A BASIC READER FOR COLLEGE WRITERS

Send book orders and requests for desk copies or supplements to:

Townsend Press
1038 Industrial Drive
Berlin, New Jersey 08009

For even faster service, call us at our toll-free number:

1-800-772-6410

Or FAX your request to:

1-609-753-0649

ISBN 0-944210-85-6

Contents

Note: For ease of reference, the title of the passage that concludes each chapter appears in parentheses.

Preface v

Introduction   1

UNIT ONE

Chapter 1   (Joseph Palmer)   **5**
Chapter 2   (A Cruel Sport)   **9**
Chapter 3   (No Luck with Women)   **13**
Chapter 4   (Accident and Recovery)   **17**
Chapter 5   (Animal Senses)   **21**

Unit One Tests   **25**

UNIT TWO

Chapter 6   (Money Problems)   **33**
Chapter 7   (The New French Employee)   **37**
Chapter 8   (A Cruel Teacher)   **41**
Chapter 9   (Learning to Study)   **45**
Chapter 10   (The Mad Monk)   **49**

Unit Two Tests   **53**

UNIT THREE

Chapter 11   (Conflict over Holidays)   **61**
Chapter 12   (Dr. Martin Luther King, Jr.)   **65**
Chapter 13   (Relating to Parents)   **69**
Chapter 14   (The Nightmare of Gym)   **73**
Chapter 15   (A Model Teacher)   **77**

Unit Three Tests   **81**

UNIT FOUR

Chapter 16   (Shoplifter)   **89**
Chapter 17   (A Nutty Newspaper Office)   **93**
Chapter 18   (Roughing It)   **97**
Chapter 19   (Getting Scared)   **101**
Chapter 20   (My Sister's Date)   **105**

Unit Four Tests   **109**

Appendixes

A Limited Answer Key   **117**

B Dictionary Use   **120**

C Word List   **122**

Preface

The problem is all too familiar: *students just don't know enough words*. Reading, writing, and content teachers agree that many students' vocabularies are inadequate to the demands of courses. Weak vocabularies limit students' understanding of what they read and the clarity and depth of what they write.

The purpose of the Townsend Press vocabulary series is to provide a solid, workable answer to the vocabulary problem. The short version of the series consists of three books, each of which *teaches* 160 important words. Within each book are 20 chapters, with 8 words in each chapter. Here are the distinctive features of IMPROVING VOCABULARY SKILLS, SHORT VERSION:

1 **An intensive words-in-context approach.** Studies show that students learn words best by seeing them repeatedly in different contexts, not through rote memorization. IMPROVING VOCABULARY SKILLS, SHORT VERSION, gives students an intensive in-context experience by presenting each word in seven different contexts. Each chapter takes students through a productive sequence of steps:

- Students first see a word in a preview.
- They then infer the meaning of the word by considering two sentences in which it appears.
- Based on their inferences, students select and confirm each word's meaning in a matching test. They are then in a solid position to further strengthen their knowledge of a word.
- Finally, they strengthen their knowledge of a word by applying it three times: in two sentence practices and in a passage practice.

Each encounter with a word brings it closer to becoming part of the student's permanent word bank.

2 **Abundant practice.** In addition to the extensive practice in each chapter, there are *four unit tests* at the end of each five-chapter unit. These tests reinforce students' knowledge of every word in every chapter. Further, there are added tests in the *Test Bank* and the *computer disks* that accompany the book. All this practice means that students learn in the surest possible way: by working closely and repeatedly with each word.

3 **Controlled feedback.** Students receive feedback on two of the practices in each vocabulary chapter. A limited answer key at the back of the book lets them see how they did with the opening preview of words. The key also provides answers for the first sentence check in the chapter. The key enables students to take an active role in their own learning. And they are likely to use the answer key in an honest and positive way if they know they may be tested on the many activities and selections for which answers are not provided. (Answers not in the book are in the Instructor's Edition. They can, of course, be copied and passed out at the teacher's discretion.)

4 **Focus on essential words.** A good deal of time and research went into selecting the 160 words featured in the book. Word frequency lists were consulted, along with lists in a wide number of vocabulary books. In addition, the authors and editors each prepared their own lists. A computer was used to help in the consolidation of the many word lists. A long process of group discussion then led to final decisions about the words that would be more helpful for students on a basic reading level.

5 **Appealing content.** Dull practice materials work against learning. On the other hand, meaningful, lively, and at times even funny sentences and passages can spark students' attention and thus encourage their grasp of the material. For this reason, a great deal of effort was put into creating sentences and passages with both widespread appeal *and* solid context support. We have tried throughout to make the practice materials truly enjoyable for teachers and students alike. Look, for example, at the passage on page 8 that closes the first chapter of this book.

6 **Clarity of format.** The book has been designed so that its very format contributes to the learning process. All eight words of a chapter appear on a single page, and each practice begins and ends on one page. In particular, each chapter has a two-page spread (turn, for example, to pages 6-7) so that students can refer to the eight words in context on one side while working on the matching test and sentence check on the other side. And a second color has been used within the book to help make the content as visually appealing as possible.

7 Supplementary materials.

a A combined *Instructor's Manual and Test Bank* is available at no charge to instructors using the book. It can be obtained by writing to the Reading Editor, Townsend Press, Pavilions at Greentree—408, Marlton, NJ 08053. This booklet contains pre- and post-tests for all four units in the text as well as teaching suggestions, a model syllabus, an answer key, and a set of mastery tests for each chapter.

b A *comprehensive series of computer disks* also accompanies the book. These disks provide up to four tests for each of the 20 vocabulary chapters. The disks are self-booting and contain a number of other user- and instructor-friendly features, including brief explanations of answers, a sound option, frequent mention of the user's first name, a running score at the bottom of the screen, and a record-keeping file.

Probably in no other area of reading instruction is the computer more useful than in reinforcing vocabulary. This vocabulary program takes full advantage of the computer's unique capabilities and motivational appeal. Here's how the program works:

- Students are tested on the eight words in a chapter, with each word in a sentence context different from any in the book itself.
- After students answer each question, they receive immediate feedback: The computer tells if a student is right or wrong and *why*, frequently using the student's first name and providing a running score.
- When the test is over, the computer supplies a test score and—this especially is what is unique about this program—a chance to retest on the specific words the student got wrong. For example, if a student misses four items on a test, the retest provides *four different sentences* that test just those four words. Students then receive a score for this special retest. What is so valuable about this, of course, is that the computer gives students added practice in the words they most need to review.
- In addition, the computer offers a *second*, more challenging test in which students must identify the meanings of the chapter words without benefit of context. This test is a final check that students have really learned the words. And, again, there is the option of a retest, tailor-made to recheck only those words missed on the first definition test.

By the end of this program, students' knowledge of each word in the chapter will have been carefully reinforced. And this reinforcement will be the more effective for having occurred in an electronic medium that especially engages today's students.

A demo disk will be sent to any teacher requesting it. The full set of disks, with unlimited copying privileges, will be available at no charge to departments adopting at least 200 copies of the book.

8 Realistic pricing. We wanted a book that would offer the highest possible quality at the best possible price. We are delighted that Townsend Press has committed to sell this book to students at a price under nine dollars. Such a modest price makes it an inexpensive supplement for any reading or writing course.

9 One in a sequence of books. IMPROVING VOCABULARY SKILLS, SHORT VERSION, is the intermediate text in a sequence that includes BUILDING VOCABULARY SKILLS, SHORT VERSION (a basic text) and ADVANCING VOCABULARY SKILLS, SHORT VERSION (a more advanced text). Suggested grade levels for each book are included in the *Instructor's Manual*. Together, the three books will help create a vocabulary foundation that will make any student a better reader, writer, and thinker.

Acknowledgments

Our thanks go to the talented group of writers and editors at Townsend Press who have worked closely with us on the book: John Langan, Joan Dunayer, Jane Mackay, and Beth Johnson Ruth. We also acknowledge the extraordinary programming efforts of Professor Terry Hutchison of Atlantic Community College. He has helped us create exactly the kind of sophisticated, comprehensive software that we believe is needed to solidify students' learning of all the words in the book. Inspiration for the cover came from an idea by Janet M. Goldstein, and the cover itself owes thanks to the artistry of Larry Didona. We appreciate as well the customized page design work of Alysse Einbender, and we are particularly grateful for the design, editing, and proofreading skills of Janet M. Goldstein.

Sherrie L. Nist   *Carole Mohr*

Introduction

WHY VOCABULARY DEVELOPMENT COUNTS

You have probably often heard it said, "Building vocabulary is important." Maybe you've politely nodded in agreement and then forgotten the matter. But it would be fair for you to ask, "Why *is* vocabulary development important? Provide some evidence." Here are four compelling bits of evidence.

1   Common sense tells you what many research studies have shown as well: vocabulary is a basic part of reading comprehension. Simply put, if you don't know enough words, you are going to have trouble understanding what you read. An occasional word may not stop you, but if there are too many words you don't know, comprehension will suffer. The *content* of textbooks is often challenge enough; you don't want to work as well on understanding the *words* that make up that content.

2   Vocabulary is a major part of almost every standardized test, including reading achievement tests, college entrance exams, and armed forces and vocational placement tests. Test authors know that vocabulary is a key measure of both one's learning and one's ability to learn. So they have a separate vocabulary section as well as a reading comprehension section. The more words you know, then, the better you are likely to do on such important tests.

3   Studies have made clear that students with strong vocabularies are more successful in school. And one widely known study found that a good vocabulary, more than any other factor, was common to people enjoying successful careers in life. Words are in fact the tools not just of better reading, but of writing, speaking, listening, and thinking as well. The more words you have at your command, the more effective your communication can be, and the more influence you can have on the people around you.

4   In the world of the 1990s, a good vocabulary will count more than ever. Far fewer people will work on farms or in factories. Far more will be in jobs that provide services or process information. More than ever, words will be the tools of our trade: words we use in reading, writing, listening, and speaking. Furthermore, experts say that workers of the 90s will be called on to change jobs and learn new skills at an ever-increasing pace. The keys to survival and success will thus be the abilities to communicate skillfully and learn quickly. A solid vocabulary is essential for both of these skills.

The evidence is overwhelming, clearly, that building vocabulary is crucial. The question then becomes, "What is the best way of going about it?"

WORDS IN CONTEXT: THE KEY TO VOCABULARY DEVELOPMENT

Memorizing lists of words is a traditional method of vocabulary development. But a person is likely to forget such memorized lists quickly. Studies show that to master a word you must see and use it in various contexts. By working actively and repeatedly with a word, you greatly increase the chance of really learning it.

The following activity will make clear how the book is organized and how it uses a words-in-context approach. Answer the questions or fill in the missing words in the spaces provided.

Contents

Turn to the table of contents on pages iii-iv.

• How many chapters are in the book? _____

• Three short sections follow the chapters. The first provides a limited answer key; the second gives helpful information on using _____; and the third is an index of the 160 words in the book.

Vocabulary Chapters

Turn to Chapter 1 on pages 5-8. This chapter, like all the others, consists of six parts:

• The *first part*, on page 5, is titled _____

This preview introduces you to the eight words covered in the chapter. After you try filling in the blanks, you are asked to check the _____ at the back and to fill in any empty blanks.

• The *second part* of the chapter, on page 6, is titled _____

The left-hand column lists the eight words. Under each word is its _____ (in parentheses) and its part of speech (*noun, verb,* or *adjective*). For example, we are told that *absolve,* the first word on page 6, is a verb.

Using the pronunciation guide requires only a bit of information: Short vowels have no special mark, while long vowels are indicated with a line above the vowel. (Note that long vowels have the sound of their own name.) What is the first word in the list with a long vowel? _____ . Symbols that sound like "uh"—like the "uh" a speaker makes when hesitating—are symbolized by the schwa (ə), which looks like an upside down *e*. What is the first word in the list with a schwa? _____. Finally, an accent mark (') tells which syllable to emphasize when pronouncing a word. What is the first word in the list with an accent on the second syllable? _____ A brief guide to the dictionary on pages 120-121 gives further information on pronouncing words.

To the right of each word are two sentences that help you understand its meaning. In each sentence, the *context* —the words surrounding the boldfaced word—provides clues you can use to figure out the definition. For example, look at the first sentence for the word *absolve.*

Some people get rich by cheating others and then think a large donation to a charity will **absolve** them of guilt.

Based on the context, what is the meaning of *absolve*?

     a. accuse   b. surprise   c. free from blame   d. send to prison

A second sentence also helps you pin down the meaning:

The mayor, accused of taking bribes, told reporters, "In the end, I'll clear my name and be **absolved** of any wrongdoing."

By looking closely at each pair of sentences, you can decide on the meaning of a word. (In the example above, *absolve* clearly means *free from blame.)* As you figure out each meaning, you are working actively with the word. You are creating the groundwork you need to understand *and* to remember the word. Getting involved with the word and developing a feel for it, based upon its use in context, is the key to word mastery.

It is with good reason, then, that the directions at the top of page 6 tell you to look _____ and _____ at the context. Doing so deepens your sense of the word and prepares you for the next activity.

• The *third part* of the chapter, on page 7, is titled _____.

According to research, it is not enough to see a word in context. At a certain point, it is important as well to see the meaning of a word. The matching test provides that meaning, but it also makes you look for and think about that meaning. In other words, it continues the active learning that is your surest route to learning and remembering a word.

Note the caution that follows the test. Do not proceed any further until you are sure that you know the correct meaning of each word.

• The *fourth part* of the chapter (also on page 7) is titled _____.

Here are eight sentences that give you an opportunity to apply your understanding of the eight words. After inserting the words, check your answers in the limited key at the back of the book. Be sure to use the answer key as a learning tool only. Doing so will help you to master the words and to prepare for the last two activities and the unit tests, for which answers are not provided.

• The *fifth part* of the chapter, on page 8, is titled _____ , and the *sixth part* is titled _____.

Both practices test you on all eight words, giving you a chance to deepen your mastery. In the second activity, you have the context of an entire passage in which you can practice and apply the words.

At the bottom of the last page of this chapter is a box where you can enter your score for the final two checks. These scores should also be entered into the vocabulary performance chart located on the inside back page of the book. To get your score, all you need do is to refer to the following scale, which appears on the last page of every chapter:

0 wrong = 100%
1 wrong = 88%
2 wrong = 75%
3 wrong = 63%
4 wrong = 50%
and so on.

You now know, in a nutshell, how to proceed with the words in each chapter. Make sure that you do each page very carefully. *Remember, as you work through the activities, you are learning the words.*

How many times in all will you use each word?   If you look, you'll see that each chapter gives you the opportunity to work with each word seven times. Each "impression" adds to the likelihood that the word will become part of your active vocabulary. You will have further opportunities to use the word in the four unit tests that follow each chapter and on the computer disks that are available with the book.

FINAL THOUGHTS

The facts are in. A strong vocabulary is a source of power. Words can make you a better reader, writer, speaker, thinker, and learner. They can dramatically increase your chances of success in school and in your job.

But words will not come automatically. They must be learned in a program of regular study. If you commit yourself to learning words, and you work actively and honestly with the chapters in this book, you will not only enrich your vocabulary—you will enrich your life as well.

Previewing the Words

Find out how many of the eight words in this chapter you already know. Try to complete each sentence with the most suitable word from the list below. Use each word once.

Leave a sentence blank rather than guessing at an answer. Your purpose here is just to get a sense of the eight words and what you may know about them.

absolve	adamant	amoral	animosity
antagonist	eccentric	encounter	malign

1. The wrestler caught his _____ by the hair and then pulled him to the mat.

2. Some criminals are _____—they truly don't care whether or not their actions are evil.

3. The book so _____(e)d the actress that she sued the author for extreme damage to her public image.

4. I was surprised to _____ Matt in a supermarket in Los Angeles, since I thought he still lived in Chicago.

5. Willy hoped the new witness would _____ him of guilt by testifying that he had been bowling the night of the murder.

6. My little sister was _____ in her refusal to go to Aunt Eva's house. She held on to the knob of her bedroom door as my mother tried to yank her loose.

7. You might think family businesses have the advantage of friendly relationships, but there is often

   great _____ between relatives who work together.

8. Florence Nightingale, the famous nursing reformer, had the _____ habit of carrying around a pet owl in one of her pockets.

Now check your answers by turning to page 117. Fix any mistakes and fill in any blank spaces by writing in the correct answers. By doing so, you will complete this introduction to the eight words.

You're now ready to strengthen your knowledge of the words you already know and to master the words you're only half sure of, or don't know at all. Turn to the next page.

Eight Words in Context

Figure out the meanings of the following eight words by looking *closely and carefully* at the context in which the words appear. Doing so will prepare you for the matching test and practices on the two pages that follow.

1 **absolve**
(ab-zolv')
-*verb*

   a. Some people get rich by cheating others and then think a large donation to a charity will **absolve** them of guilt.

   b. The mayor, accused of taking bribes, told reporters, "In the end, I'll clear my name and be **absolved** of any wrongdoing."

2 **adamant**
(ad'-ə-mənt)
-*adjective*

   a. Ron is **adamant** about not changing plans. He insists we still camp out even though the weather report now says it will be cold and rainy.

   b. **Adamant** in his support of gun control, Senator Keen won't give in to pressure from the powerful people who tried to silence him.

3 **amoral**
(ə-môr'-əl)
-*adjective*

   a. Jerry is almost totally **amoral**. He cares only about making money and having fun and couldn't care less about right or wrong.

   b. A former president of Uganda, Idi Amin, was truly **amoral**. Lacking ethical principles, he jailed, tortured and killed innocent opponents.

4 **animosity**
(an'-ə-mos'-ə-tē)
-*noun*

   a. I was shocked when Sandy said she hated Lionel. I'd never realized she felt such **animosity** toward him.

   b. Ill will between the two families went back so many generations that nobody remembers what originally caused the **animosity**.

5 **antagonist**
(an-tag'-ə-nist)
-*noun*

   a. At the divorce hearing, the husband and wife were such bitter **antagonists** that it was hard to believe they once loved each other.

   b. In the ring, the two boxers were **antagonists**, but in their private lives they were good friends.

6 **eccentric**
(ik-sen'-trik)
-*adjective*

   a. Bruce is quite **eccentric**. For example, he lives in a circular house and drives to work on a motorcycle, in a three-piece suit.

   b. Perhaps more of us would be **eccentric** in more ways if we didn't worry so much about being considered odd.

7 **encounter**
(en-koun'-tər)
-*verb*

   a. Some people claim to have **encountered** space aliens, but there is no convincing evidence of such meetings.

   b. I dislike returning to my small hometown, where I am likely to **encounter** people who knew me as a troubled kid.

8 **malign**
(mə-līn')
-*verb*

   a. Stacy continually **maligns** her ex-husband. The way she describes him, you'd think he was a cross between a mass murderer and a blockhead.

   b. Those who say the female crocodile eats her young **malign** her. She simply takes them into a protective pouch inside her mouth.

Matching Words and Definitions

Check your understanding of the eight words by matching each word with its definition. Look back at the sentences in "Eight Words in Context" as needed to decide on the meaning of each word.

_____ 1. **absolve**	a.	firm in opinion or purpose; stubborn
_____ 2. **adamant**	b.	without principles; uncaring about right and wrong
_____ 3. **amoral**	c.	odd; out of the ordinary
_____ 4. **animosity**	d.	to clear of guilt or blame
_____ 5. **antagonist**	e.	to meet unexpectedly; come upon
_____ 6. **eccentric**	f.	an opponent; one who opposes or competes
_____ 7. **encounter**	g.	a strong dislike; hatred; ill will
_____ 8. **malign**	h.	to make false statements that harm a reputation; speak evil of

CAUTION: Do not go any further until you are sure the above answers are correct. If you have studied the "Eight Words in Context," you will know how to match each word. Then you can use the matches to help you in the following practices. Your goal is to reach a point where you don't need to check definitions at all.

➤ Sentence Check 1

Complete each sentence below with the most suitable word from the box. Use each word once.

absolve	adamant	amoral	animosity
antagonist	eccentric	encounter	malign

1. Lilly was _____ in her belief that Sam was faithful. Even lipstick on his cheek didn't weaken her faith in him.

2. My brothers had planned to meet in the department store, but they _____(e)d each other in the parking lot.

3. I'm tired of hearing the two candidates for mayor _____ each other with stupid insults.

4. The congressman is so _____ that he'll make promises to get elected and then break them whenever it suits him.

5. Lena often says cruel things and then apologizes afterwards, but a mere "I'm sorry" doesn't remove the hurt or _____ her of guilt.

6. The owners of the department store were always competing with each other. They acted more like _____s than partners.

7. I avoid serious discussions with my sister because she shows great _____ toward me if I don't share her opinion.

8. When my mother attended high school, female students who took wood shop were considered _____. Now, however, it's not odd for women to learn carpentry.

Now check your answers to these questions by turning to page 117. Going over the answers carefully will help you prepare for the next two checks, for which answers are not given.

➤ Sentence Check 2

Complete each sentence below with two words from the box. Use each word once.

absolve	adamant	amoral	animosity
antagonist	eccentric	encounter	malign

1-2. The _____ millionaire dressed so shabbily that anyone who

_____(e)d him thought he was poor.

3-4. Her brother feels such _____ toward Carol that he never says a single kind thing

about her; he only _____s her.

5-6. The congresswoman was _____ in her opposition to the nuclear power plant. She

didn't back down even when facing the toughest _____.

7-8. Wayne is so _____ that he doesn't even have the desire to be

_____(e)d of guilt for all the times he has lied, cheated, and stolen.

➤ Final Check: Joseph Palmer

Here is a final opportunity for you to strengthen your knowledge of the eight words. First read the following passage carefully. Then fill in each blank with a word from the box at the top of this page. (Context clues will help you figure out which word goes in which blank.) Use each word once.

In 1830, a Massachusetts farmer named Joseph Palmer moved to the city, only to find that people continually reacted to him with anger and hatred. Why was this? Palmer certainly wasn't a(n) (1)_____ man. No, he had a strong sense of right and wrong, and he was both friendly and helpful to others. Yet his neighbors would cross to the other side of the street when they (2)_____(e)d him. Children insulted Palmer and sometimes threw stones at him. Grown men hurled rocks through the windows of his house. Even the local minister (3)_____(e)d Palmer, telling the congregation that Palmer admired only himself.

One day, four men carrying scissors and a razor attacked Palmer and threw him to the ground. Pulling out a pocketknife, Palmer fought back, slashing at their legs. His (4)_____s fled. Afterward, Palmer was the one arrested and jailed. While in jail he was attacked two more times. Both times, he fought his way free. After a year—although his accusers still wouldn't (5)_____ him of guilt—he was released.

Palmer had won. The cause of all the (6)_____ and abuse had been his long, flowing beard. Palmer, (7)_____ to the end, had refused to shave.

By thirty years after Palmer's difficulties, it was no longer (8)_____ to wear whiskers. Among the many who wore beards then was the President of the United States, Abraham Lincoln.

SCORES: Sentence Check 2 _____ %   **Final Check** _____ %
Enter your scores above and in the vocabulary performance chart on the inside back cover of the book.

Number right: 8 = 100%   7 = 88%   6 = 75%   5 = 63%   4 = 50%   3 = 38%   2 = 25%   1 = 13%

Previewing the Words

Find out how many of the eight words in this chapter you already know. Try to complete each sentence with the most suitable word from the list below. Use each word once.

Leave a sentence blank rather than guessing at an answer. Your purpose here is just to get a sense of the eight words and what you may know about them.

acclaim	elicit	engross	escalate
exploit	obsolete	tangible	terminate

1. The invention of electricity soon made gaslight _____.

2. A wedding ring is a(n) _____ expression of a couple's commitment to each other.

3. Sometimes an article I'm reading on the bus will _____ me so much that I pass my stop.

4. Peter's jokes are in such bad taste that they _____ looks of disgust instead of laughter.

5. "We need to _____ our fund-raising efforts," the theater manager said. "Otherwise, the company won't survive."

6. Dustin Hoffman's performance in *Rain Man* won him an Oscar and the _____ of admiring critics.

7. When Luke was caught stealing money from the company, his employment was

   _____(e)d, and he was brought up on criminal charges.

8. At the turn of the century, factory owners _____(e)d children by making them work in terrible conditions for as many as eighteen hours a day.

Now check your answers by turning to page 117. Fix any mistakes and fill in any blank spaces by writing in the correct answers. By doing so, you will complete this introduction to the eight words.

You're now ready to strengthen your knowledge of the words you already know and to master the words you're only half sure of, or don't know at all. Turn to the next page.

Eight Words in Context

Figure out the meanings of the following eight words by looking *closely and carefully* at the context in which the words appear. Doing so will prepare you for the matching test and practices on the two pages that follow.

1 **acclaim**
(ə-klām')
-*noun*

   a. Any subway system that is clean, quiet, and safe deserves **acclaim**.

   b. Although Vincent Van Gogh is now considered a genius, the artist received little **acclaim** in his lifetime.

2 **elicit**
(i-lis'-it)
-*verb*

   a. Elizabeth Taylor's violet eyes always **elicit** admiration and wonder.

   b. Wes is such a troublemaker in Mrs. Turner's class that his late arrival one day **elicited** this sharp comment from her: "In your case, Wes, never is better than late."

3 **engross**
(en-grōs')
-*verb*

   a. The TV movie so **engrossed** Bryan that he didn't even budge when he was called to dinner.

   b. The fascinating single-file march of black ants along the sidewalk **engrossed** me for several minutes.

4 **escalate**
(es'-kə-lāt')
-*verb*

   a. The fight between the two hockey players **escalated** into an all-out battle among members of both teams.

   b. Male turkeys challenge each other by strutting with tails spread like fans. As the contest **escalates** and they get more excited, their naked heads turn blue.

5 **exploit**
(eks-ploit')
-*verb*

   a. Some wealthy people obtained their money when they **exploited** individuals less fortunate than themselves.

   b. Ricky **exploited** the fact that his parents were out of town for two days by having a wild, two-day party at home.

6 **obsolete**
(ob'-sə-lēt')
-*adjective*

   a. Word processors have made typewriters almost **obsolete**.

   b. In the United States, the automobile quickly made travel by horse and carriage **obsolete**.

7 **tangible**
(tan'-jə-bəl)
-*adjective*

   a. The sculptor loved making her ideas **tangible** by giving them form in metal and stone.

   b. Corn-chip crumbs, empty soda bottles, and dirty napkins were **tangible** evidence that a party had taken place the night before.

8 **terminate**
(tûr'-mə-nāt')
-*verb*

   a. The students waited patiently for the bell to **terminate** Mr. Leeman's boring lecture.

   b. The referee should have **terminated** the boxing match when he first saw the weaker fighter losing the ability to defend himself.

Matching Words and Definitions

Check your understanding of the eight words by matching each word with its definition. Look back at the sentences in "Eight Words in Context" as needed to decide on the meaning of each word.

_____ 1. **acclaim**	a. to draw forth
_____ 2. **elicit**	b. to stop; bring to an end
_____ 3. **engross**	c. able to be touched; having form and matter
_____ 4. **escalate**	d. no longer in use or practice; out-of-date
_____ 5. **exploit**	e. to increase or intensify
_____ 6. **obsolete**	f. enthusiastic praise or applause; great approval
_____ 7. **tangible**	g. to hold the full attention of
_____ 8. **terminate**	h. to use selfishly or unethically; take unfair advantage of

CAUTION: Do not go any further until you are sure the above answers are correct. If you have studied the "Eight Words in Context," you will know how to match each word. Then you can use the matches to help you in the following practices. Your goal is to reach a point where you don't need to check definitions at all.

➤ Sentence Check 1

Complete each sentence below with the most suitable word from the box. Use each word once.

acclaim	elicit	engross	escalate
exploit	obsolete	tangible	terminate

1. The perfect crime leaves no _____ clues.

2. If solar energy becomes as cheap and plentiful as sunshine, nuclear energy may become

   _____ .

3. Only Hank's essay received the teacher's _____; all the other papers received negative comments.

4. The shouting match between Rose and her brother _____(e)d until it was so loud that the neighbors complained.

5. I never read a novel in bed at night because it may _____ me so much that I'll stay up half the night trying to finish it.

6. When teachers feel _____(e)d, they often go on strike for larger salaries and better working conditions.

7. Sometimes the only way to _____ a faulty computer program is by shutting off the machine. Otherwise, the program may keep repeating itself endlessly.

8. In one disturbing survey, the question "Which do you like better, Daddy or TV?"

   _____(e)d this response from a number of children: "TV."

Now check your answers to these questions by turning to page 117. Going over the answers carefully will help you prepare for the next two checks, for which answers are not given.

➤Sentence Check 2

Complete each sentence below with two words from the box. Use each word once.

acclaim	elicit	engross	escalate
exploit	obsolete	tangible	terminate

1-2. The gifted ice skater's routine _____(e)d the audience. At the end, he _____(e)d a burst of applause with a long, rapid spin.

3-4. Although hand-crafted furniture is almost _____, mass production hasn't yet _____(e)d all demand for it.

5-6. Workers want such _____ rewards as money and a pension, but they also welcome less concrete benefits, such as _____ for a job well done.

7-8. The more the British _____(e)d the American colonies by taxing them unfairly, the more the anti-British sentiment _____(e)d among the colonists.

➤Final Check: A Cruel Sport

Here is a final opportunity for you to strengthen your knowledge of the eight words. First read the following passage carefully. Then fill in each blank with a word from the box at the top of this page. (Context clues will help you figure out which word goes in which blank.) Use each word once.

The room lights dimmed, and a spotlight revealed a short, fat man holding a heavy chain. He tugged the chain and a muzzled bear appeared. The man, the animal's owner, announced that the bear's name was Sally. He would give a hundred dollars, he said, to anyone who wrestled Sally to the floor. Alex, sitting in the nightclub audience, was shocked. He had thought bear wrestling was (1)_____, given up long ago as a cruel sport.

The offer (2)_____(e)d an eager response. "Let me try it!" one man called. The audience showed its (3)_____ for the event by cheering him on. He went up and started to swing at Sally. She tried to back away. The match greatly (4)_____(e)d most members of the audience, who watched every move.

"Knock her on her rear!" the owner shouted. When Sally finally raised a leg to defend herself, her owner jerked her back with a sharp tug. Sally's opponent then saw that she had no claws. He thus felt more confident, so his attack (5)_____(e)d. When the man fighting the bear seemed likely to pin Sally, her owner allowed the bear to throw him off. At that, the owner (6)_____(e)d the match, calling out "Next!"

Another man then sprang to his feet. And soon another. The same type of match took place six more times— with the same results.

Finally, the owner led Sally away. Her drooped head and labored walk were (7)_____ expressions of the animal's misery. Alex was more certain than ever that bear-wrestling (8)_____(e)d the animal for human entertainment. As Sally passed his table, Alex heard her soft moans. He then saw that the bear was old, and completely blind.

SCORES: **Sentence Check 2** _____%   **Final Check** _____%
Enter your scores above and in the vocabulary performance chart on the inside back cover of the book.

Number right: 8 = 100%   7 = 88%   6 = 75%   5 = 63%   4 = 50%   3 = 38%   2 = 25%   1 = 13%

Previewing the Words

Find out how many of the eight words in this chapter you already know. Try to complete each sentence with the most suitable word from the list below. Use each word once.

Leave a sentence blank rather than guessing at an answer. Your purpose here is just to get a sense of the eight words and what you may know about them.

allusion	altruistic	appease	arbitrary
assail	banal	euphemism	mercenary

1. The two candidates continuously _____(e)d each other with accusations of fraud.

2. "Gail isn't the only athlete in the family," Clarence said, making a(n) _____ to Gail's father, a bowling champion.

3. My mother will never say directly that someone has "died"; instead, she always uses the

   _____ "passed away."

4. A(n) _____ person might prefer a low-paying job with a charitable organization over a high-paying corporate job.

5. The boss's decision to fire Nora was not at all _____. Company rules clearly state that her behavior was unacceptable.

6. The question "How are you doing?" is so overused that it's even hard to ask it sincerely without

   sounding _____.

7. My cousin has always been openly _____. At the age of ten, he answered "What do you want to be when you grow up?" with a single word: "Rich."

8. When the customer returned, angry at having bought a broken clock, the salesman quickly

   _____(e)d her by giving her a full refund.

Now check your answers by turning to page 117. Fix any mistakes and fill in any blank spaces by writing in the correct answers. By doing so, you will complete this introduction to the eight words.

You're now ready to strengthen your knowledge of the words you already know and to master the words you're only half sure of, or don't know at all. Turn to the next page.

Eight Words in Context

Figure out the meanings of the following eight words by looking *closely and carefully* at the context in which the words appear. Doing so will prepare you for the matching test and practices on the two pages that follow.

1 **allusion**
(ə-lōo'-zhən)
-*noun*

   a. After I suggested that Monty have fruit for dessert instead of chocolate cake, he responded, "Is that an **allusion** to my weight?"

   b. Ray didn't have the courage to come right out and ask Lucy to marry him. Instead, he only made an **allusion** to marriage by asking, "Wouldn't it be easier if we had to fill out just one tax form?"

2 **altruistic**
(al'-trōo-is'-tik)
-*adjective*

   a. "I'm not often **altruistic**," Brett admitted. "I usually put my own welfare first."

   b. When an enemy approaches, ground squirrels show **altruistic** behavior. They risk their own lives to give alarm calls to nearby relatives.

3 **appease**
(ə-pēz')
-*verb*

   a. My sister was so outraged when I accidentally scratched her favorite old Beatles record that nothing I could say or do would **appease** her.

   b. Roger was furious when he saw me out with another guy, but I quickly **appeased** him by explaining that the "date" was my cousin.

4 **arbitrary**
(or'-bi-trer'-ē)
-*adjective*

   a. Professor Miller's students were angry that he graded essays in an **arbitrary** way, rather than using precise standards.

   b. Parents should not impose and enforce rules according to their moods. Such **arbitrary** discipline only confuses and angers children.

5 **assail**
(ə-sāl')
-*verb*

   a. The storm **assailed** us with hail and heavy rains.

   b. The press **assailed** the company responsible for the oil spill until it increased its efforts to clean up the mess.

6 **banal**
(bə-nal')
-*adjective*

   a. The film, with its overused expressions and commonplace plot, was the most **banal** I had ever seen.

   b. "Nice to see you" may be a **banal** comment, but what it lacks in originality it makes up for in friendliness.

7 **euphemism**
(yōo'-fə-miz'-əm)
-*noun*

   a. Common **euphemisms** include "final resting place" (for *grave*), "intoxicated" (for *drunk*), and "powder room" and "comfort station" (for *toilet*).

   b. The Central Intelligence Agency is on record as having referred to assassination with the **euphemism** "change of health."

8 **mercenary**
(mûr'-sə-ner'-ē)
-*adjective*

   a. Ed is totally **mercenary**. His philosophy is, "Pay me enough, and I'll do anything."

   b. The con man pretended to love the wealthy widow, but he actually married her for **mercenary** reasons.

Matching Words and Definitions

Check your understanding of the eight words by matching each word with its definition. Look back at the sentences in "Eight Words in Context" as needed to decide on the meaning of each word.

_____ 1. **allusion**

_____ 2. **altruistic**

_____ 3. **appease**

_____ 4. **arbitrary**

_____ 5. **assail**

_____ 6. **banal**

_____ 7. **euphemism**

_____ 8. **mercenary**

a. determined by personal judgment, not rule or reason; based on impulse

b. motivated only by financial gain; greedy

c. an indirect reference

d. a substitute for a direct word or phrase considered offensive

e. to bring to a state of calm or peace, especially by providing what is demanded

f. lacking originality; overused; commonplace

g. to attack physically or verbally

h. unselfishly concerned for the welfare of others; unselfish

CAUTION: Do not go any further until you are sure the above answers are correct. If you have studied the "Eight Words in Context," you will know how to match each word. Then you can use the matches to help you in the following practices. Your goal is to reach a point where you don't need to check definitions at all.

➤Sentence Check 1

Complete each sentence below with the most suitable word from the box. Use each word once.

allusion	altruistic	appease	arbitrary
assail	banal	euphemism	mercenary

1. There have been people _____ enough to sell their own children for the right price.

2. "Someone hasn't shown me his report card," my mother said, making a(n) _____ to my brother.

3. It takes a(n) _____ person to adopt a handicapped child.

4. Madge is a tough debater who _____s the opposing side with sharp questions and arguments.

5. The local undertaker insists on using a(n) _____ for the chapel of his funeral parlor. He calls it "the slumber room."

6. The only thing that would _____ the dead boy's parents was imprisonment of the drunk driver who had killed him.

7. The judge's sentence was _____. Rather than being based on past similar cases or on the seriousness of the crime, it was based on the judge's opinion of the defendant.

8. "You're special" probably appears on thousands of greeting cards, but when someone says it to you and means it, it never seems _____.

Now check your answers to these questions by turning to page 117. Going over the answers carefully will help you prepare for the next two checks, for which answers are not given.

➤ Sentence Check 2

Complete each sentence below with two words from the box. Use each word once.

allusion	altruistic	appease	arbitrary
assail	banal	euphemism	mercenary

1-2. _____ people tend to place the public's welfare above their own self-interest. In

contrast, _____ people will sell even harmful products to make a profit.

3-4. The parents of a girl who had been suspended _____(e)d the principal with charges of

incompetence. The principal finally _____(e)d them by showing them the teacher's
report of the girl's behavior.

5-6. My boss judges performance in a(n) _____ manner, praising and scolding according to

his moods. And if he wants me to work late for an hour or so, he uses this _____:
"Please stay a few minutes longer today."

7-8. Instead of writing a(n) _____ comment such as "That ballerina is light on her feet,"

the critic made this interesting _____ to the dancer's movements: "She was never
heavier than moonlight."

➤ Final Check: No Luck with Women

Here is a final opportunity for you to strengthen your knowledge of the eight words. First read the following
passage carefully. Then fill in each blank with a word from the box at the top of this page. (Context clues will
help you figure out which word goes in which blank.) Use each word once.

I don't have much luck with women. The other night at a singles dance, I asked an attractive lady,
"Excuse me, do you have the time?" (I admit the question is a bit (1)_____, but I couldn't
think of anything more clever.) She answered, "Isn't that kind of personal?" Another woman got really upset
just because I asked, "Haven't we met before, at Weight Watchers?" Okay, so I was wrong. I didn't mean to
make a(n) (2)_____ to her size. Still, after that, nothing I said or did helped at all to
(3)_____ her.

Women don't appreciate how nice I am. First of all, I'm not particularly (4)_____.
For instance, I've never considered a woman's wealth the most important thing about her. It's the second
most important thing. I'm so (5)_____ that I once took care of a guy who was drunk by
sending him home in a cab. Instead of being grateful, his attractive date (who had been in the ladies' room)
(6)_____(e)d me with all sorts of accusations. How was I supposed to know she was his
wife?

When I ask women out, they often answer me with (7)_____s such as "I'm busy" or
"I already have plans." What they really mean is, "I'm busy making plans to avoid you."

Women's behavior is totally (8)_____. At least, I can't see any reason to it. Last
night, for example, a woman I was nice enough to treat to a Coke threw it in my face. Thank goodness, she
didn't get any on my day-glo Mickey Mouse tie.

SCORES: Sentence Check 2 _____ %   Final Check _____ %
Enter your scores above and in the vocabulary performance chart on the inside back cover of the book.

Number right: 8 = 100%   7 = 88%   6 = 75%   5 = 63%   4 = 50%   3 = 38%   2 = 25%   1 = 13%

Previewing the Words

Find out how many of the eight words in this chapter you already know. Try to complete each sentence with the most suitable word from the list below. Use each word once.

Leave a sentence blank rather than guessing at an answer. Your purpose here is just to get a sense of the eight words and what you may know about them.

calamity	comprehensive	fluctuate	persevere
ponder	rehabilitate	turmoil	venture

1. If you _____ in your good study habits, you will be able to pass chemistry.

2. At tomorrow's staff meeting, I will _____ saying what I really think and cross my fingers that I don't get fired.

3. Peter's moods _____ wildly. One minute he feels totally happy; the next, he wishes he had never been born.

4. Most prisons, short on money, make little effort to _____ inmates so that they can lead productive, wholesome lives upon release.

5. Hurricane Camille was a _____—along the coasts of Louisiana, Mississippi, and Alabama, 241 people died.

6. Ricardo asked the librarian for a _____ tour of the library so that he would learn how to locate any materials he might need in the future.

7. In _____ over the absence of a teacher, the sixth-grade class quickly came to order when the principal entered the room.

8. At age 16, I would sit on our backyard swing and _____ life and death and whether Bobby Giordano liked me or not.

Now check your answers by turning to page 117. Fix any mistakes and fill in any blank spaces by writing in the correct answers. By doing so, you will complete this introduction to the eight words.

You're now ready to strengthen your knowledge of the words you already know and to master the words you're only half sure of, or don't know at all. Turn to the next page.

Eight Words in Context

Figure out the meanings of the following eight words by looking *closely and carefully* at the context in which the words appear. Doing so will prepare you for the matching test and practices on the two pages that follow.

1 **calamity**
(kə-lam'-i-tē)
-*noun*

a. The earthquake survivors slowly rebuilt their homes and lives after the **calamity**.

b. Our neighbor's house burned down one night in May. Ever since that **calamity**, the children have been afraid to go to bed at night.

2 **comprehensive**
(kom'-prē-hen'-siv)
-*adjective*

a. That article on sightseeing in New Orleans was not **comprehensive**. It failed to mention many points of interest in that wonderful city.

b. The company's **comprehensive** medical insurance plan covers most health services, including hospitals, doctors, and dentists.

3 **fluctuate**
(fluk'-chōō-āt')
-*verb*

a. My weight used to **fluctuate** between 150 and 190 pounds. Now it's steady, at 170 pounds.

b. Desert temperatures can **fluctuate** between the day and the night by as much as 50 degrees.

4 **persevere**
(pûr'-sə-vîr')
-*verb*

a. "I know you're tired," Jack said, "but we've got to **persevere** and get to the camp before the storm hits."

b. It was not easy to attend English classes while working two jobs, but Nina **persevered** until she could speak English well.

5 **ponder**
(pon'-dər)
-*verb*

a. Too often we don't take time to **ponder** the possible consequences of our actions.

b. Over the years, Mr. Madigan rarely took time to **ponder** life. Since his heart attack, however, he's thought a lot about what is important to him.

6 **rehabilitate**
(rē'-hə-bil'-ə-tāt')
-*verb*

a. To **rehabilitate** people who have lost the ability to work, it is necessary to stress good work habits as well as job skills.

b. My grandfather learned to walk, write, and speak again in a program that **rehabilitates** stroke victims.

7 **turmoil**
(tûr'-moil)
-*noun*

a. There was much **turmoil** among the passengers when a sudden blizzard shut down all flights coming to and leaving the airport.

b. After the **turmoil** of crying babies, active children, and trying to feed 120 people, I'm glad when our family reunions end.

8 **venture**
(ven'-chər)
-*verb*

a. "I'll **venture** any ride in this amusement park except the Twister," said Nick. "I'll risk getting sick to my stomach, but I won't risk my life."

b. Sue has decided to **venture** her security by giving up her job and starting her own business.

Matching Words and Definitions

Check your understanding of the eight words by matching each word with its definition. Look back at the sentences in "Eight Words in Context" as needed to decide on the meaning of each word.

_____ 1. **calamity**

_____ 2. **comprehensive**

_____ 3. **fluctuate**

_____ 4. **persevere**

_____ 5. **ponder**

_____ 6. **rehabilitate**

_____ 7. **turmoil**

_____ 8. **venture**

a. to risk; take the risks of

b. including much; taking much or everything into account

c. to restore to a normal life through therapy and/or education

d. to continue with an effort or plan despite difficulties

e. complete confusion; uproar

f. a disaster; an event of great loss and misery

g. to vary irregularly

h. to consider carefully; think deeply about

CAUTION: Do not go any further until you are sure the above answers are correct. If you have studied the "Eight Words in Context," you will know how to match each word. Then you can use the matches to help you in the following practices. Your goal is to reach a point where you don't need to check definitions at all.

➤ Sentence Check 1

Complete each sentence below with the most suitable word from the box. Use each word once.

calamity	comprehensive	fluctuate	persevere
ponder	rehabilitate	turmoil	venture

1. Iris is so vain that she considers it a _____ if a pimple appears anywhere on her face.

2. Too many people have a child without taking time to _____ parenthood. They give less thought to having a baby than to buying a sofa.

3. Our psychology exam will be _____; it will cover everything we've studied since September.

4. Learning the computer program was difficult, but when Maria realized how useful it would be in her work, she was glad she had _____ (e)d.

5. It took many months to _____ my aunt after she lost her sight, but now she can get around her home and neighborhood on her own.

6. The day we moved, the apartment was in _____. Boxes and people seemed to be constantly on the move, and the baby wouldn't stop crying.

7. The way my dog's appetite _____ (e)d this week worries me. One day she hardly ate anything, and the next she gulped down everything I gave her.

8. Instead of hiring a lawyer, the defendant will _____ pleading her own case in court.

Now check your answers to these questions by turning to page 117. Going over the answers carefully will help you prepare for the next two checks, for which answers are not given.

➤ Sentence Check 2

Complete each sentence below with two words from the box. Use each word once.

calamity	comprehensive	fluctuate	persevere
ponder	rehabilitate	turmoil	venture

1-2. The one time my cousin _____(e)d skydiving, the result was a

_____. Her parachute didn't open, and she was injured so badly in the fall that she

almost died.

3-4. The drug-treatment center can _____ most addicts. Among the failures are addicts

who don't _____ with the treatment and leave the center early.

5-6. "We need to _____ all we might do to help families in trouble," said the social worker

to her staff. "We must plan a _____ program, not just a narrow plan dealing with one

part of their lives."

7-8. Our boss's moods and orders _____ so wildly at times that they throw the office into

_____.

➤ Final Check: Accident and Recovery

Here is a final opportunity for you to strengthen your knowledge of the eight words. First read the following
passage carefully. Then fill in each blank with a word from the box at the top of this page. (Context clues will
help you figure out which word goes in which blank.) Use each word once.

Anna's eccentric behavior led to a (1)_____ that changed her life forever. Before we

could stop her, she dove off a rock into a river that wasn't deep enough. When she hit the bottom, she broke

her back.

I visited Anna at the hospital almost every day for the next few weeks. I saw her mood

(2)_____ wildly between severe anger and quiet depression. Her whole life seemed in

(3_____; she was too confused and troubled to think reasonably about her future.

Within about a month, however, I began to see a change in Anna. She had moved to Henner House to

participate in a (4)_____ program, designed to meet all the needs of patients like Anna.

The program (5)_____s accident victims so that they can return to fulfilling lives. Anna

gained hope once she saw she could learn to do such everyday tasks as cooking, cleaning, and bathing. After

learning how to get around indoors, she (6)_____(e)d traveling around the city in her

wheelchair. The more she did, the better she felt. The staff also helped Anna plan for her future. They urged

her to (7)_____ her goals and how she might meet them. At times, it was difficult for her

to (8)_____ with the program, but she didn't quit.

Now, ten months later, Anna is able to do many of the ordinary things she used to do—work, drive, and

live in an apartment with a friend. Yes, her life has changed forever. But Anna is once again glad to be alive.

SCORES:	Sentence Check 2 _____ %	Final Check _____ %

Enter your scores above and in the vocabulary performance chart on the inside back cover of the book.

Number right: 8 = 100%   7 = 88%   6 = 75%   5 = 63%   4 = 50%   3 = 38%   2 = 25%   1 = 13%

Previewing the Words

Find out how many of the eight words in this chapter you already know. Try to complete each sentence with the most suitable word from the list below. Use each word once.

Leave a sentence blank rather than guessing at an answer. Your purpose here is just to get a sense of the eight words and what you may know about them.

attest	attribute	discern	enhance
exemplify	mobile	nocturnal	orient

1. My nephew's favorite toys are the _____ ones, those that can walk, jump, or travel on wheels.

2. When my china clown broke, I glued it back together so carefully that no one could

   _____ the crack.

3. The positions of the stars help sailors _____ themselves on the open seas.

4. Because its climate is too cold for most germs, Antarctica has the _____ of being nearly germ-free.

5. Parents, serving as role models, usually _____ adulthood to their children.

6. Good communication skills will _____ a career in any field.

7. I know when my brother has enjoyed one of his _____ feasts because I find a stack of dishes in the sink in the morning.

8. Witnesses _____ to the fact that rainfall makes the ground of Death Valley so slippery that boulders slide across it.

Now check your answers by turning to page 117. Fix any mistakes and fill in any blank spaces by writing in the correct answers. By doing so, you will complete this introduction to the eight words.

You're now ready to strengthen your knowledge of the words you already know and to master the words you're only half sure of, or don't know at all. Turn to the next page.

Eight Words in Context

Figure out the meanings of the following eight words by looking *closely and carefully* at the context in which the words appear. Doing so will prepare you for the matching test and practices on the two pages that follow.

1 **attest**
(ə-test')
-verb

   a. Anyone who has seen the Golden Gate Bridge in the rose-gold light of sunset can **attest** to its beauty.

   b. My uncle, a New York City policeman, can **attest** to the existence of bullet-proof clipboards.

2 **attribute**
(at'-rə-byōōt')
-noun

   a. A 300-page novel written in 1939 has the odd **attribute** of containing no *e*, the most common letter in English.

   b. In Japan, some cars have such computerized **attributes** as windshield wipers that automatically turn on when it rains.

3 **discern**
(di-sûrn')
-verb

   a. An experienced jeweler can **discern** almost immediately whether a diamond is genuine or fake.

   b. People who are red-green colorblind can **discern** the colors of traffic lights by recognizing shades of gray.

4 **enhance**
(en-hans')
-verb

   a. Our gym teacher **enhanced** her appearance with a more attractive hairstyle.

   b. The college catalogue stated that the writing course would "**enhance** all students' writing skills" by improving their grammar and style.

5 **exemplify**
(ig-zem'-plə-fī')
-verb

   a. The many IRS employees who give citizens inaccurate information **exemplify** government incompetence.

   b. Mr. Pell, who emphasizes original thinking and freedom of expression, **exemplifies** the best in teaching.

6 **mobile**
(mō'-bəl)
-adjective

   a. My parents own a **mobile** home, which can be moved from place to place on a long truck.

   b. When I was a bedridden hospital patient, the highlight of my days was the **mobile** library that a volunteer wheeled into my room each morning.

7 **nocturnal**
(nok-tûr'-nəl)
-adjective

   a. The painting was of a restful **nocturnal** scene. Lamplit houses were set against a night sky.

   b. Being **nocturnal**, owls are rarely seen during the day.

8 **orient**
(ôr'-ē-ent)
-verb

   a. When coming up from the subway, I often need to look at a street sign to **orient** myself.

   b. Drivers of the future may **orient** themselves in unfamiliar places with the help of an electronic map that shows the car's location.

Matching Words and Definitions

Check your understanding of the eight words by matching each word with its definition. Look back at the sentences in "Eight Words in Context" as needed to decide on the meaning of each word.

_____ 1. **attest**   a. of, about, or happening in the night; active at night

_____ 2. **attribute**   b. to give evidence; bear witness; testify

_____ 3. **discern**   c. to determine the location or direction of

_____ 4. **enhance**   d. to recognize; make out clearly

_____ 5. **exemplify**   e. to improve

_____ 6. **mobile**   f. moving or able to move from place to place

_____ 7. **nocturnal**   g. a quality or feature of a person or thing

_____ 8. **orient**   h. to be an example of; represent; be typical of

CAUTION: Do not go any further until you are sure the above answers are correct. If you have studied the "Eight Words in Context," you will know how to match each word. Then you can use the matches to help you in the following practices. Your goal is to reach a point where you don't need to check definitions at all.

➤ Sentence Check 1

Complete each sentence below with the most suitable word from the box. Use each word once.

attest	attribute	discern	enhance
exemplify	mobile	nocturnal	orient

1. Fresh garlic may not _____ the breath, but it certainly improves spaghetti sauce.

2. A witness _____(e)d to the truth of the defendant's claim that she had loved the murdered man.

3. The lives of such reformers as Susan B. Anthony, Gandhi, and Martin Luther King _____ greatness.

4. The convicts decided on a(n) _____ escape. The darkness would hide them as they fled through the forest.

5. Sue's hairpiece is so natural looking that it's impossible to _____ where the hairpiece ends and her own hair begins.

6. Birds use the angle of the sun and stars to help them _____ themselves during their long migrations.

7. My mother is unable to walk, but with her wheelchair she is _____ enough to get around her one-story home, move along a sidewalk, and even shop at a mall.

8. Giant kelp, a form of seaweed, has some amazing _____s. Not only is it the world's fastest-growing vegetable, but the more it is cut, the faster it grows.

Now check your answers to these questions by turning to page 117. Going over the answers carefully will help you prepare for the next two checks, for which answers are not given.

➤ Sentence Check 2

Complete each sentence below with two words from the following list. Use each word once.

attest	attribute	discern	enhance
exemplify	mobile	nocturnal	orient

1-2. Because Helen Keller could not hear or see, the senses she did have were _____(e)d by keen use. It is said that she could _____ who was in a room simply by smell.

3-4. A _____ robot that collects and delivers mails throughout our office building _____s itself with electric eyes.

5-6. In fables, animals often illustrate human _____s. In the story of the tortoise and the hare, the slow tortoise is meant to _____ the human quality of being slow but steady.

7-8. Anyone who has ever gone to college can _____ to the fact that, during finals, many students become _____ animals, staying up all night before an exam and then sleeping during the day after taking it.

➤ Final Check: Animal Senses

Here is a final opportunity for you to strengthen your knowledge of the eight words. First read the following passage carefully. Then fill in each blank with a word from the box at the top of this page. (Context clues will help you figure out which word goes in which blank.) Use each word once.

Animals possess sensory powers that humans lack. Homing pigeons fly with great speed and accuracy when they deliver messages to faraway places. How do pigeons (1)_____ themselves in unfamiliar regions? The mystery is partly explained by a pigeon's ability to see ultraviolet light, which reveals the sun's position even through clouds. In addition, pigeons can hear sound waves that have traveled hundreds of miles. These waves (2)_____ a pigeon's sense of direction by indicating distant mountains and seas. Pigeons even appear to (3)_____ changes in the Earth's magnetic field.

Bats have (4)_____s no less impressive. As (5)_____ animals, they search for food in complete darkness. They do so by screeching in tones higher than any human can hear and then locating prey by the returning echoes.

Scorpions also (6)_____ the night hunter. Tiny leg hairs allow them to instantly feel vibrations in the sand made by a (7)_____ insect as far as two feet away.

People with knowledge of the pigeon, bat and scorpion can (8)_____ to the fact that such "inventions" as the magnetic compass, radar, and the motion detector are nothing new.

SCORES: Sentence Check 2 _____%   **Final Check** _____%
Enter your scores above and in the vocabulary performance chart on the inside back cover of the book.

Number right: 8 = 100%   7 = 88%   6 = 75%   5 = 63%   4 = 50%   3 = 38%   2 = 25%   1 = 13%

UNIT ONE: Test 1

PART A
Choose the word that best completes each sentence and write it in the space provided.

1. **acclaim**
   attribute
   euphemism
   turmoil

   A common _____ for *corpse* is "remains."

2. **rehabilitate**
   attest
   ponder
   exemplify

   The counseling program to _____ addicts includes job training.

3. **altruistic**
   banal
   nocturnal
   obsolete

   According to legend, vampires are _____ creatures who fear daylight.

4. **elicits**
   appeases
   escalates
   absolves

   In the winter, the price of tomatoes _____ while their quality goes down.

5. **mercenary**
   arbitrary
   mobile
   obsolete

   The taxi driver was so _____ that he charged his own mother for rides.

6. **adamant**
   mercenary
   tangible
   obsolete

   You probably thought that mail delivery by mule was _____, but it still exists in the Grand Canyon.

7. **Nocturnal**
   Altruistic
   Amoral
   Comprehensive

   _____ enough to refuse to take money from the public for his discovery of X-rays, Wilhelm Roentgen died poor.

8. **allusion**
   animosity
   calamity
   attribute

   The sinking of the ship *Titanic,* which struck an iceberg, was a(n) _____ in which nearly 1,600 people died.

9. **animosity**
   calamity
   turmoil
   acclaim

   Although Marilyn Monroe received great praise from fans and critics, she never received the _____ of an Academy Award.

10. **assailed**
    enhanced
    pondered
    absolved

    The model realized if she wanted to be _____ of the charges, she'd better hire a detective to find the real murderer.

(Continues on next page)

PART B
Circle **C** if the italicized word is used **correctly**. Circle **I** if the word is used **incorrectly**.

C   I   11.   It's hard to *discern* the differences between the Field twins.

C   I   12.   The Olympic swimmer *pondered* across the pool in record time.

C   I   13.   The man *attested* to his crime, pleading guilty to all charges.

C   I   14.   Every day, people *enhance* the tropical rain forests by destroying some 20,000 acres.

C   I   15.   Students often *exploit* the presence of a substitute teacher by using fake names.

C   I   16.   It's healthier to stay the same weight than to *fluctuate* up and down.

C   I   17.   The passerby showed his *animosity* by entering the burning house and pulling the child to safety.

C   I   18.   If you worry about the environment, you're *eccentric*. According to a poll, over three-fourths of Americans do.

C   I   19.   In 1876, Wild Bill Hickok was in a poker game that was *terminated* by a bullet entering the back of his head.

C   I   20.   It's much harder to define the words for *tangible* things such as love and intelligence than it is to define terms for physical objects such as chairs and cars.

> *SCORE:* (Number correct) _____ x 5 = _____ %

Enter your scores above and in the vocabulary performance chart on the inside back cover of the book.

UNIT ONE: Test 2

Complete each sentence with a word from the box. Use each word once.

adamant	allusion	amoral	antagonist	appease
attribute	comprehensive	elicit	orient	persevere

1. Marathon runners must _____ beyond the point at which they start to feel pain.

2. People who can't read are able to _____ themselves in a city by relating to familiar places, not signs.

3. In some religions, gods and goddesses represent various human _____s, such as strength, beauty, and wisdom.

4. Despite all the wars that have taken place, England and Portugal have never faced each other as wartime _____s.

5. Apparently, the chance to be President wouldn't _____ much enthusiasm from most Americans—89 percent say they wouldn't want the job.

6. It's often said that Nature is _____, but humans are part of nature, and most of them *do* care about right and wrong.

7. To get a bachelor's degree from certain universities, students must take a _____ exam that tests their overall knowledge of their major field.

8. Our congressional representative, _____ in her opposition to pesticides, often reminds voters that pesticides kill about 14,000 people each year.

9. In a(n) _____ to the city's varied population, our professor mentioned that more than half of the city's newspapers are in languages other than English.

10. When Kathleen stood up Evan for the prom, an apology did not _____ him. He's suing her for the cost of his rented tux and the prom tickets.

(Continues on next page)

27

PART B

Circle **C** if the italicized word is used **correctly.** Circle **I** if the word is used **incorrectly.**

C   I   11.   Cory was so *engrossed* in the film that he fell asleep.

C   I   12.   The *turmoil* of a smooth, clear lake always makes me feel a similar peace.

C   I   13.   Our veterinarian has a *mobile* office, a fully equipped van which she drives to patients' homes.

C   I   14.   In my dreams I *venture* to perform feats that I would never dare when awake, such as leaping from roof to roof down a row of houses.

C   I   15.   When, during our drive, we *encountered* an unexpected hailstorm, we felt as if we were inside a metal can being pelted with stones.

C   I   16.   The critic *maligned* the folk singer by saying her voice has both richness and sparkle, like velvet trimmed with gold.

C   I   17.   In 1971, three dolphins *assailed* a drowning woman by keeping her afloat and protecting her from sharks across 200 miles of ocean.

C   I   18.   When the evidence in a case is unclear, a jury's decision may be *arbitrary,* based only on the jurors' "gut feeling."

C   I   19.   Alice Walker's novel The Color Purple won both the Pulitzer Prize and the National Book Award because critics found the novel so *banal.*

C   I   20.   Lightning bolts, which travel at millions of miles an hour and produce five times the heat of the sun's surface, *exemplify* Nature's tremendous energy.

SCORE: (Number correct) _____ x 5 = _____ %

Enter your scores above and in the vocabulary performance chart on the inside back cover of the book.

UNIT ONE: Test 3

PART A: Synonyms
In the space provided, write the letter of the choice that is most nearly the **same** in meaning as the boldfaced word.

_____ 1. **tangible**　　**a)** movable　　**b)** spiritual　　**c)** calm　　**d)** touchable

_____ 2. **calamity**　　**a)** invention　　**b)** anger　　**c)** tragedy　　**d)** event

_____ 3. **attest**　　**a)** testify　　**b)** teach　　**c)** respond　　**d)** stain

_____ 4. **elicit**　　**a)** state　　**b)** attack　　**c)** draw out　　**d)** avoid

_____ 5. **allusion**　　**a)** problem　　**b)** reference　　**c)** behavior　　**d)** insult

_____ 6. **fluctuate**　　**a)** lean　　**b)** vary　　**c)** prevent　　**d)** stand still

_____ 7. **encounter**　　**a)** meet　　**b)** buy　　**c)** continue despite difficulties　　**d)** depend

_____ 8. **ponder**　　**a)** recognize　　**b)** think over　　**c)** use　　**d)** refuse

_____ 9. **arbitrary**　　**a)** illegal　　**b)** governed by law　　**c)** odd　　**d)** based on impulse

_____ 10. **exemplify**　　**a)** praise　　**b)** excuse　　**c)** illustrate　　**d)** send for

_____ 11. **obsolete**　　**a)** personal　　**b)** old-fashioned　　**c)** noisy　　**d)** commonplace

_____ 12. **antagonist**　　**a)** opponent　　**b)** supporter　　**c)** question　　**d)** response

_____ 13. **exploit**　　**a)** assist　　**b)** abuse　　**c)** leave　　**d)** increase

_____ 14. **euphemism**　　**a)** quotation　　**b)** main point　　**c)** trait　　**d)** inoffensive term

_____ 15. **orient**　　**a)** consider carefully　　**b)** please　　**c)** continue　　**d)** locate

_____ 16. **appease**　　**a)** end　　**b)** calm down　　**c)** take advantage of　　**d)** begin

_____ 17. **discern**　　**a)** distinguish mentally　　**b)** forget　　**c)** interest　　**d)** deny

_____ 18. **rehabilitate**　　**a)** repeat　　**b)** come upon　　**c)** restore to normality　　**d)** clear of guilt

_____ 19. **attribute**　　**a)** confusion　　**b)** characteristic　　**c)** regret　　**d)** ill will

_____ 20. **venture**　　**a)** dare　　**b)** increase　　**c)** improve　　**d)** intrude on

(Continues on next page)

PART B: Antonyms
In the space provided, write the letter of the choice that is most nearly the **opposite** in meaning to the boldfaced word.

_____21. **nocturnal**   a) early   b) late   c) normal   d) by day

_____22. **altruistic**   a) unfriendly   b) selfish   c) usual   d) not well-known

_____23. **comprehensive** a) interesting   b) puzzling   c) narrow   d) obvious

_____24. **assail**   a) avoid   b) continue   c) stop   d) defend

_____25. **enhance**   a) prove   b) worsen   c) support   d) resist

_____26. **acclaim**   a) statement   b) recognition   c) criticism   d) assistance

_____27. **banal**   a) original   b) old   c) orderly   d) unselfish

_____28. **amoral**   a) dependable   b) calm   c) ethical   d) based on personal choice

_____29. **mobile**   a) medical   b) immovable   c) harmful   d) cautious

_____30. **absolve**   a) blame   b) solve   c) bring to a state of peace   d) annoy

_____31. **eccentric**   a) nearby   b) generous   c) ordinary   d) disorganized

_____32. **persevere**   a) build   b) add to   c) blame   d) quit

_____33. **animosity**   a) spirituality   b) beauty   c) opposition   d) friendliness

_____34. **engross**   a) delight   b) bore   c) make active   d) discourage

_____35. **adamant**   a) straightforward   b) greedy   c) enormous   d) flexible

_____36. **escalate**   a) lessen   b) lift   c) cause   d) form an opinion

_____37. **mercenary**   a) rich   b) unusual   c) generous   d) careless

_____38. **terminate**   a) begin   b) study   c) pay attention to   d) compete

_____39. **malign**   a) recover   b) praise   c) be consistent   d) move

_____40. **turmoil**   a) admiration   b) peace and quiet   c) blessing   d) reality

SCORE: (Number correct) _____ x 2.5 = _____ %

Enter your scores above and in the vocabulary performance chart on the inside back cover of the book.

UNIT ONE: *Test 4*

PART A
Complete each sentence in a way that clearly shows you understand the meaning of the boldfaced word. Take a minute to plan your answer before you write.

Example: Being **nocturnal** animals, raccoons _____ *raid our garbage cans only at night.*

1. The news reported a **calamity** in which _____

_____

2. One day typewriters will become **obsolete** because _____

_____

3. Three personal **attributes** that I possess are _____

_____

4. One **tangible** indication of affection is _____

_____

5. When I take a bath, I often **ponder** _____

_____

6. The **eccentric** teacher has a habit of _____

_____

7. One advantage of a **mobile** library might be _____

_____

8. The most **altruistic** thing I ever saw anyone do was to _____

_____

9. The actor received this **acclaim** for his performance: " _____

_____

10. I plan to **persevere** in _____

_____

(Continues on next page)

PART B

After each boldfaced word are a *synonym* (a word that means the same as the boldfaced word), an *antonym* (a word that means the opposite of the boldfaced word), and a word that is neither. Mark the synonym with an *S* and the antonym with an *A*.

Example: **enhance**   ___S___ improve   _____ lead   ___A___ weaken

11-12. **persevere**   _____ look   _____ stop   _____ persist

13-14. **comprehensive**   _____ limited   _____ broad   _____ irregular

15-16. **terminate**   _____ end   _____ begin   _____ grow

17-18. **amoral**   _____ ethical   _____ costly   _____ unprincipled

19-20. **assail**   _____ flow   _____ attack   _____ defend

PART C

Use five of the following ten words in sentences. Make it clear that you know the meaning of the word you use. Feel free to use the past tense or plural form of a word.

absolve	animosity	antagonist	appease	banal
encounter	engross	euphemism	mercenary	turmoil

21. _____

_____

22. _____

_____

23. _____

_____

24. _____

_____

25. _____

SCORE: (Number correct) _____ x 4 = _____ %

Enter your scores above and in the vocabulary performance chart on the inside back cover of the book.

Previewing the Words

Find out how many of the eight words in this chapter you already know. Try to complete each sentence with the most suitable word from the list below. Use each word once.

Leave a sentence blank rather than guessing at an answer. Your purpose here is just to get a sense of the eight words and what you may know about them.

| concurrent | confiscate | constitute | decipher |
| default | nominal | predominant | prerequisite |

1. My kids think that pizza, peanut butter, hot dogs, and soda _____ the four basic food groups.

2. Some nightclubs charge only a _____ entrance fee but a fortune for each drink.

3. Knowing basic math skills is a _____ for learning the more advanced concepts of algebra.

4. Do doctors take a course to learn how to write prescriptions which nobody but the pharmacist can

   _____?

5. Diana had a chance of winning the swim marathon, but she _____(e)d by not signing up in time.

6. Anger and frustration were the _____ emotions among students when they heard that tuition would be raised again.

7. Because their classes are _____, Brad and Rene can conveniently take turns driving each other to campus.

8. The police officer would _____ illegal fireworks from teenagers and then set them off at his own home on July 4.

Now check your answers by turning to page 117. Fix any mistakes and fill in any blank spaces by writing in the correct answers. By doing so, you will complete this introduction to the eight words.

You're now ready to strengthen your knowledge of the words you already know and to master the words you're only half sure of, or don't know at all. Turn to the next page.

Eight Words in Context

Figure out the meanings of the following eight words by looking *closely and carefully* at the context in which the words appear. Doing so will prepare you for the matching test and practices on the two pages that follow.

1 **concurrent**
(kən-kûr´-ənt)
-*adjective*

   a. Having mistakenly registered for two **concurrent** classes, Joe had to change one class to a different time.

   b. Just when the town's steel mill closed, a new toy factory opened. If the two events had not been **concurrent**, half the town would be unemployed.

2 **confiscate**
(kon´-fis-kāt´)
-*verb*

   a. Not only did the teacher **confiscate** the note I passed to my boyfriend, but she also read it out loud to the entire class.

   b. Chinese drug agents once **confiscated** $2 million worth of heroin wrapped in plastic and inserted into live goldfish. The agents took possession of the drugs as they were being sent out of the country.

3 **constitute**
(kon´-sti-tōot´)
-*verb*

   a. A good movie, a pizza, and animated conversation **constitute** my idea of a perfect night out.

   b. Twelve business and professional people **constitute** the board of directors of the local women's shelter.

4 **decipher**
(di-sī´-fər)
-*verb*

   a. Why do contracts have to use language that's so difficult to **decipher**?

   b. On one of Holly's essays, her English teacher wrote, "Please type your papers. I can't **decipher** your handwriting."

5 **default**
(di-fôlt´)
-*verb*

   a. We won our case against the appliance repairman because he **defaulted** by failing to appear in court.

   b. Jay's mother said, "I'll co-sign on your car loan, but you have to make every payment. If you **default**, it will hurt my credit rating."

6 **nominal**
(nom´-ə-nəl)
-*adjective*

   a. Apart from a **nominal** registration fee, the camp for needy children is entirely free.

   b. Professor Banks gave only **nominal** extra credit for participating in psychology experiments. She wanted our course grade to be based primarily on our test scores.

7 **predominant**
(pri-dom´-ə-nənt)
-*adjective*

   a. Rock is the **predominant** music in our dorm, but country music is also popular.

   b. Though the **predominant** type of car in New York City in 1900 used gasoline, a third of the cars ran on electricity.

8 **prerequisite**
(prē-rek´-wi-zit)
-*noun*

   a. You can't take Spanish Literature I unless you've taken the **prerequisite**, Spanish III.

   b. Do you think it was right for Kathy to tell Joel that his quitting smoking was a **prerequisite** for their marriage?

Matching Words and Definitions

Check your understanding of the eight words by matching each word with its definition. Look back at the sentences in "Eight Words in Context" as needed to decide on the meaning of each word.

_____ 1. **concurrent**	a. to make up; be the parts of
_____ 2. **confiscate**	b. to fail do something required
_____ 3. **constitute**	c. most common or noticeable
_____ 4. **decipher**	d. something required beforehand
_____ 5. **default**	e. to take or seize with authority
_____ 6. **nominal**	f. to interpret or read (something confusing or hard to make out)
_____ 7. **predominant**	g. slight; very small compared to what might be expected
_____ 8. **prerequisite**	h. happening or existing at the same time

CAUTION: Do not go any further until you are sure the above answers are correct. If you have studied the "Eight Words in Context," you will know how to match each word. Then you can use the matches to help you in the following practices. Your goal is to reach a point where you don't need to check definitions at all.

➤ Sentence Check 1

Complete each sentence below with the most suitable word from the box. Use each word once.

concurrent	confiscate	constitute	decipher
default	nominal	predominant	prerequisite

1. The _____ clothing style in our high schools is jeans and T-shirts.

2. Although the two robberies were _____, one man had planned them both.

3. One hundred senators and 435 members of the House of Representatives _____the United States Congress.

4. A _____ for taking the driver-education class is passing a written test on the driving laws.

5. The town library charges only a _____ fine for late books but a higher fine for late videotapes.

6. Derek has such terrible handwriting that his wife couldn't _____ his message saying she should meet him at the restaurant.

7. The phone company refused to install a phone in Glen's new apartment because he had

   _____(e)d in paying a bill on his last account.

8. In 1988, the United States government tried to seize any boat carrying drugs. The Coast Guard even

   _____(e)d a yacht carrying less than a tenth of an ounce of marijuana.

Now check your answers to these questions by turning to page 117. Going over the answers carefully will help you prepare for the next two checks, for which answers are not given.

➤ Sentence Check 2

Complete each sentence below with two words from the box. Use each word once.

concurrent	confiscate	constitute	decipher
default	nominal	predominant	prerequisite

1-2. In the summer, local children can sign up for art or music lessons for the _____ fee of $3. It's impossible to take both, though, since the classes will be _____.

3-4. Although cancer and heart disease _____ the leading threats to life in the U.S., car accidents are the _____ cause of death for teenagers.

5-6. "It seems as if a degree in accounting is a _____ for understanding our tax laws," said Ken. "Who else can really _____ the tax codes?"

7-8. The small print for my farm mortgage loan stated that if I should _____ on payments, the bank had the right to _____ the farm.

➤ Final Check: Money Problems

Here is a final opportunity for you to strengthen your knowledge of the eight words. First read the following passage carefully. Then fill in each blank with a word from the box at the top of this page. (Context clues will help you figure out which word goes in which blank.) Use each word once.

"My car has been stolen!" My neighbor, Martha, ran into my house crying and angry. "I saw them take it."

I called the police for her, and she told an officer the license number and car model. "The (1)_____ color of the car is brown," she added, "but it has a black roof. I saw two men steal it. They just towed it away."

"You saw them tow it?" the officer asked. "Have you (2)_____(e)d in paying your car loan?"

"What do you mean?" Martha asked.

"If you haven't been making your payments, the bank or dealer has the right to (3)_____ the car."

Martha admitted that she hadn't paid her loan in three months. Later she told me she'd gotten notices in the mail but threw them away because their language was too complicated to (4)_____. She also said she was having money problems. (5)_____ with the car loan was a big home improvement loan. She also had five credit-card bills and regular living expenses to pay. She was about $12,000 in debt.

At my suggestion, Martha visited a debt counselor who helped her develop a plan to pay her bills. The only (6)_____s for receiving this free service were a regular job and a willingness to pay one's debts in full. The counselor told her what would (7)_____ a reasonable budget, based on her income and expenses. They then wrote to the companies she owed to arrange to pay a (8)_____ amount each month until the whole debt was paid.

Now, Martha is getting back on her feet again—in more ways than one, since she never got the car back.

SCORES: Sentence Check 2 _____ %   Final Check _____ %
Enter your scores above and in the vocabulary performance chart on the inside back cover of the book.

Number right: 8 = 100%   7 = 88%   6 = 75%   5 = 63%   4 = 50%   3 = 38%   2 = 25%   1 = 13%

Previewing the Words

Find out how many of the eight words in this chapter you already know. Try to complete each sentence with the most suitable word from the list below. Use each word once.

Leave a sentence blank rather than guessing at an answer. Your purpose here is just to get a sense of the eight words and what you may know about them.

degenerate	implausible	incoherent	intricate
sanctuary	sinister	suffice	vulnerable

1. The class discussion on abortion soon _____(e)d into a shouting match.

2. Because they tend to have brittle bones, the elderly are _____ to fractures.

3. It's _____ that a college student could party every night and still make the dean's list.

4. In the movie, a mad scientist thought up the _____scheme of releasing a deadly virus. His evil plot failed when he died from the virus himself.

5. Ken's cartoons _____ for the school newspaper, but they wouldn't be good enough for the city papers.

6. My brother talks a lot in his sleep, but he's so _____ that we can never figure out what he's saying.

7. My bedroom is a(n) _____ from the constant noises of the television and stereo throughout our apartment.

8. At the concert, I sat behind a woman with a(n) _____ hairstyle. Numerous intertwined braids wound about the back of her head.

Now check your answers by turning to page 117. Fix any mistakes and fill in any blank spaces by writing in the correct answers. By doing so, you will complete this introduction to the eight words.

You're now ready to strengthen your knowledge of the words you already know and to master the words you're only half sure of, or don't know at all. Turn to the next page.

Eight Words in Context

Figure out the meanings of the following eight words by looking *closely and carefully* at the context in which the words appear. Doing so will prepare you for the matching test and practices on the two pages that follow.

1 **degenerate**
(di-jen'-ər-āt')
-verb

    a. Mr. Freedman's family was called to the nursing home when the old man's condition began to **degenerate**.

    b. Mel's relationship with his parents **degenerated** when he dropped out of school and became a bartender.

2 **implausible**
(im-plô'-zə-bəl)
-adjective

    a. As **implausible** as it may sound, Southern Florida sometimes does get snow.

    b. Insurance companies hear such **implausible** excuses for auto accidents as "I hit the telephone pole when I was blinded by the lights of a flying saucer."

3 **incoherent**
(in'-kō-hîr'-ənt)
-adjective

    a. If Mitch drinks much more, he'll become completely **incoherent**. His slurred speech is already difficult to understand.

    b. In a terrible nightmare, a huge red spider is about to leap on my husband, but my warning is so **incoherent** that he doesn't understand me.

4 **intricate**
(in'-tri-kit)
-adjective

    a. *War and Peace* is a long, **intricate** novel that weaves together the detailed life stories of many individuals.

    b. It's amazing to see the **intricate** gold and silver jewelry that ancient Indians made with only simple tools. It obviously required great patience and skill to create such complex ornaments.

5 **sanctuary**
(sangk'-chōō-er'-ē)
-noun

    a. Old, unused trains in Grand Central Station have served as a nighttime **sanctuary** for some of New York City's homeless.

    b. When the houseful of children becomes too noisy, Ned finds the laundry room to be a **sanctuary**, a place where he can read in quiet.

6 **sinister**
(sin'-is-ter)
-adjective

    a. Actor Edward G. Robinson often played such **sinister** characters as gangsters and Nazi spies.

    b. The novel *Rosemary's Baby* concerns the **sinister** plans of a group of devil-worshippers.

7 **suffice**
(sə-fīs')
-verb

    a. The amount of research you've done may **suffice** for a high school term paper, but not for a college one.

    b. The lift I get from attending the mid-winter flower show will have to **suffice** until springtime.

8 **vulnerable**
(vul'-nər-ə-bəl)
-adjective

    a. Homes in heavily wooded areas are especially **vulnerable** to termites.

    b. Alligators are most **vulnerable** in their soft underbellies.

Matching Words and Definitions

Check your understanding of the eight words by matching each word with its definition. Look back at the sentences in "Eight Words in Context" as needed to decide on the meaning of each word.

_____ 1. **degenerate**   a. having many parts arranged in a complicated way; complex

_____ 2. **implausible**   b. to be enough; be good enough

_____ 3. **incoherent**   c. to worsen; deteriorate

_____ 4. **intricate**   d. a place of safety, protection, or relief

_____ 5. **sanctuary**   e. open to injury or harm; sensitive; susceptible

_____ 6. **sinister**   f. difficult to believe

_____ 7. **suffice**   g. evil; wicked

_____ 8. **vulnerable**   h. not connected in an orderly, logical manner; unable to speak in an orderly, logical way

CAUTION: Do not go any further until you are sure the above answers are correct. If you have studied the "Eight Words in Context," you will know how to match each word. Then you can use the matches to help you in the following practices. Your goal is to reach a point where you don't need to check definitions at all.

➤ *Sentence Check 1*

Complete each sentence below with the most suitable word from the box. Use each word once.

degenerate	implausible	incoherent	intricate
sanctuary	sinister	suffice	vulnerable

1. The leftover meatloaf will _____ for tomorrow's lunch.

2. The Joker's name is misleading, for he's a(n) _____ man who takes pleasure in doing evil.

3. People who live in big cities are more _____ to muggings than are residents of small towns.

4. The leaves outside the window created a(n) _____ lacy shadow on my bedroom wall.

5. Although it seems _____, the seemingly dead desert really does blossom after a rainstorm.

6. People who open their home as a _____ to an escaped convict may face criminal charges themselves.

7. My husband was so upset that he was _____. It wasn't until he calmed down that I understood he had been fired.

8. When I don't have company over, my apartment tends to _____ into a jumble of papers, clothes, and school supplies.

Now check your answers to these questions by turning to page 117. Going over the answers carefully will help you prepare for the next two checks, for which answers are not given.

➤ Sentence Check 2

Complete each sentence below with two words from the box. Use each word once.

degenerate	implausible	incoherent	intricate
sanctuary	sinister	suffice	vulnerable

1-2.   Birds feel _____ to attack when they are out in the open. To attract them to your

birdfeeder, put it near a _____ of trees and large bushes.

3-4.   To get into the party, Mitch made up a(n) _____ story about having lost our invitations

in a fire. Surprisingly, the unlikely tale _____(e)d to get us in.

5-6.   When a complicated musical piece is played by a talented orchestra, audiences can appreciate its

_____ structure. But when poor musicians try the piece, it _____s

into nothing more than noise.

7-8.   The bank clerk had been so frightened by the _____ appearance of the armed man in a

ski mask that her report of the event was _____. Only after she calmed down did the

police fully understand her story.

➤ Final Check: The New French Employee

Here is a final opportunity for you to strengthen your knowledge of the eight words. First read the following passage carefully. Then fill in each blank with a word from the box at the top of this page. (Context clues will help you figure out which word goes in which blank.) Use each word once.

One summer, Nan worked in a factory with an employee recently arrived from France, a young man named Jean-Louis. He spoke little English, but Nan's basic French (1)_____(e)d for simple conversations and helpful translations.

One day, Nan was called to the foreman's office. FBI agents were there with Jean-Louis. After explaining that Jean-Louis may have been more (2)_____ than the innocent young man he appeared to be, the foreman asked her to translate for the agents. The agents said Jean-Louis had been on the run since several jewel thefts in France. Nan struggled to translate their questions, which were often too (3)_____ for her limited vocabulary. At times, she became so nervous that her speech was nearly (4)_____. When the message finally got across, Jean-Louis claimed he was being mistaken for his no-good twin brother, a story the angry FBI agents found (5)_____. The conversation soon (6)_____d until everyone was shouting at poor Nan.

Nan excused herself and went to the ladies' room, a (7)_____ from the agents and Jean-Louis. After they left, she calmed down and went back to work. But she felt (8)_____ for days as she wondered if she were under suspicion as well.

SCORES: Sentence Check 2 _____ %   **Final Check** _____ %
Enter your scores above and in the vocabulary performance chart on the inside back cover of the book.

Number right: 8 = 100%   7 = 88%   6 = 75%   5 = 63%   4 = 50%   3 = 38%   2 = 25%   1 = 13%

Previewing the Words

Find out how many of the eight words in this chapter you already know. Try to complete each sentence with the most suitable word from the list below. Use each word once.

Leave a sentence blank rather than guessing at an answer. Your purpose here is just to get a sense of the eight words and what you may know about them.

blatant	blight	garble	gloat
immaculate	plagiarism	qualm	retaliate

1. Trash is a(n) _____ on this neighborhood. The streets and sidewalks are filthy.

2. A good scrubbing with baking soda got my tea-stained mug _____.

3. I no longer feel any _____s about the times I skipped high school to go to the movies.

4. My daughter _____(e)d Alex's message so badly that I went to meet him at the wrong place and time.

5. The boy's dislike of the food was all too _____. He told the hostess it tasted "like burnt dirt."

6. When Mary told about Flo's secret love affair, Flo _____(e)d by telling their friends about Mary's affair.

7. "It's bad enough that you always beat me at bowling," one player told the other. "Then when you

   _____, you hurt my pride again."

8. Not only was Tyler wrong to commit _____, but he was also foolish to choose to copy into his report parts of the class textbook.

Now check your answers by turning to page 118. Fix any mistakes and fill in any blank spaces by writing in the correct answers. By doing so, you will complete this introduction to the eight words.

You're now ready to strengthen your knowledge of the words you already know and to master the words you're only half sure of, or don't know at all. Turn to the next page.

Eight Words in Context

Figure out the meanings of the following eight words by looking *closely and carefully* at the context in which the words appear. Doing so will prepare you for the matching test and practices on the two pages that follow.

1 **blatant**
(blā'-tənt)
-adjective

  a. Scott's smoking habit is **blatant**. His clothes smell of smoke, and nicotine has stained his fingers.

  b. The company's disregard of the environment is **blatant**. It makes no effort to stop polluting coastal waters with garbage.

2 **blight**
(blīt)
-noun

  a. Nothing has hurt our country more than the **blight** of drugs.

  b. Is TV mainly a **blight** that dulls minds or a valuable source of information?

3 **garble**
(gar'-bəl)
-verb

  a. The typesetter accidentally **garbled** the newspaper story, giving the reader only a mixed-up article.

  b. The company had **garbled** the bike's assembly instructions so badly that we were constantly confused about which step to do next.

4 **gloat**
(glōt)
-verb

  a. The coach told his team, "There's only one thing worse than a sore loser, and that's a mean winner. Don't **gloat**."

  b. Neil's sister always tattles on him and then **gloats** when he's punished.

5 **immaculate**
(i-mak'-yə-lit)
-adjective

  a. It's amazing that Carolyn always appears **immaculate**, yet her apartment often seems very dirty.

  b. Don't expect a child to come home from a birthday party with **immaculate** clothing.

6 **plagiarism**
(plā'-jə-riz'-əm)
-noun

  a. When the author saw a movie with the same plot as one of her novels, she sued for **plagiarism**.

  b. The teacher warned her students that using an author's exact words as one's own is **plagiarism**.

7 **qualm**
(kwom)
-noun

  a. Larry had no **qualms** about stealing from the cafeteria cash register. He didn't even feel guilty when someone else was blamed.

  b. After hiding Lori's bike as an April Fool's joke, I began to have **qualms**. What if she thought it was stolen and called the police?

8 **retaliate**
(ri-tal'-ē-āt')
-verb

  a. When I broke my sister's Prince record, she **retaliated** by cutting the cord of my Sony Walkman earphones.

  b. After the Baker brothers squirted some girls with soda, the girls **retaliated** by spraying the boys with cologne.

Matching Words and Definitions

Check your understanding of the eight words by matching each word with its definition. Look back at the sentences in "Eight Words in Context" as needed to decide on the meaning of each word.

_____ 1. **blatant**   a. a feeling of discomfort about a point of conscience, honor, or what is proper

_____ 2. **blight**   b. to mix up or confuse (as a story or message); scramble

_____ 3. **garble**   c. to express or feel spiteful pleasure or self-satisfaction

_____ 4. **gloat**   d. something that weakens, damages, or destroys

_____ 5. **immaculate**   e. taking someone else's writings or ideas and using them as one's own

_____ 6. **plagiarism**   f. to return injury for an injury; pay back

_____ 7. **qualm**   g. very obvious, often offensively so

_____ 8. **retaliate**   h. perfectly clean

CAUTION: Do not go any further until you are sure the above answers are correct. If you have studied the "Eight Words in Context," you will know how to match each word. Then you can use the matches to help you in the following practices. Your goal is to reach a point where you don't need to check definitions at all.

➤ *Sentence Check 1*

Complete each sentence below with the most suitable word from the box. Use each word once.

blatant	blight	garble	gloat
immaculate	plagiarism	qualm	retaliate

1. A(n) _____ house may be a sign that someone has nothing better to do than clean.

2. Child abuse is an awful _____ on the physical and mental health of our youth.

3. My aunt refuses to drive Mr. Elson to bingo because he _____s so much when he wins, which is often.

4. The F's and D's on my brother's report card are _____ evidence of how little he has studied this term.

5. I bought an answering machine because my children have _____(e)d several important phone messages.

6. Every time the Hatfields harmed the McCoys, the McCoys would _____, so the feud went on for years.

7. I would feel guilty if I called in sick when I wasn't, but no one else in the office seems to have any

_____s about doing that.

8. Mark Twain jokingly claimed that charges of _____ were ridiculous because no one can be completely original. He wrote, "We mortals can't create—we can only copy."

Now check your answers to these questions by turning to page 118. Going over the answers carefully will help you prepare for the next two checks, for which answers are not given.

➤Sentence Check 2

Complete each sentence below with two words from the box. Use each word once.

blatant	blight	garble	gloat
immaculate	plagiarism	qualm	retaliate

1-2. The living room looked _____ except for a lump under the carpet, a _____ sign that my son had taken a shortcut in cleaning up.

3-4. After the bully struck him, Jules wanted to _____ by throwing a rock, but he had _____s about doing anything so dangerous.

5-6. "At least I know you aren't guilty of _____," said my teacher. "Nobody else would have _____(e)d the report so badly that it's impossible to follow."

7-8. Willie is a _____ on the school's good name. Not only does he start fights with opposing players on the basketball court, but he also _____s after he's benched, as if he's proud of causing trouble.

➤Final Check: A Cruel Teacher

Here is a final opportunity for you to strengthen your knowledge of the eight words. First read the following passage carefully. Then fill in each blank with a word from the box at the top of this page. (Context clues will help you figure out which word goes in which blank.) Use each word once.

It has been twenty years since I was in Mr. Brill's tenth grade biology class, but I still get nervous thinking about it. Mr. Brill was a tall, bony man who resembled the skeleton at the back of the room. His meanness was (1)_____. He would call on the shyest kids to answer the most difficult questions, and when they nervously (2)_____(e)d their answers, he would clearly (3)_____. He seemed to create situations just to make us miserable. For example, if our fingernails were not (4)_____, we were sent out of class. As if we needed clean hands to dissect a frog! One time I worked extremely hard on a paper for class, but he accused me of (5)_____. He said I must have copied it because I was too dumb to write anything that good. Without a (6)_____, he gave me an F. All of us students would imagine ways to get even with him, but we were too afraid to (7)_____. In all these years since, I've never met a person who was such a (8)_____ on the personal growth of students.

SCORES: Sentence Check 2 _____%   Final Check _____%
Enter your scores above and in the vocabulary performance chart on the inside back cover of the book.

Number right: 8 = 100%   7 = 88%   6 = 75%   5 = 63%   4 = 50%   3 = 38%   2 = 25%   1 = 13%

9

Previewing the Words

Find out how many of the eight words in this chapter you already know. Try to complete each sentence with the most suitable word from the list below. Use each word once.

Leave a sentence blank rather than guessing at an answer. Your purpose here is just to get a sense of the eight words and what you may know about them.

curtail	devastate	digress	incentive
incorporate	indispensable	intermittent	succumb

1. My girlfriend is usually cheerful, but she experiences _____ periods of depression.

2. The showing of our home movies was _____(e)d when the projector broke halfway through.

3. The insurance company offers the _____ of a free vacation to salespeople who reach a certain sales figure.

4. The news that their young daughter had been on the plane that crashed _____(e)d the Crains.

5. When you're writing a paper, a good dictionary is _____ for checking the spelling and definitions of words.

6. Max is a strong-willed man. Once he makes up his mind to do something, I don't think he'll

   _____ to temptation.

7. Since my brother and I live next door to each other, we've _____(e)d our back yards into one big playground for our children.

8. The novel lost my interest whenever the author _____(e)d from the plot to explain some of the customs of the period in which the story takes place.

Now check your answers by turning to page 118. Fix any mistakes and fill in any blank spaces by writing in the correct answers. By doing so, you will complete this introduction to the eight words.

You're now ready to strengthen your knowledge of the words you already know and to master the words you're only half sure of, or don't know at all. Turn to the next page.

Eight Words in Context

Figure out the meanings of the following eight words by looking *closely and carefully* at the context in which the words appear. Doing so will prepare you for the matching test and the practices on the two pages that follow.

1 **curtail**
(kər-tāl')
-verb

  a. Upon hearing reports of a tornado, our boss **curtailed** the meeting so we all could go home early.

  b. I need to **curtail** my volunteer activities so that I can spend more time earning money to pay back a loan.

2 **devastate**
(dev'-əs-tāt')
-verb

  a. Learning that their son had been arrested for armed robbery **devastated** the Huttons.

  b. Vera is so fond of Andy. She'll be **devastated** to hear he has cancer.

3 **digress**
(di-gres')
-verb

  a. Professor Rubin never **digresses** during a lecture. Even his jokes relate to the day's topic.

  b. I tried teaching my three-year-old his phone number, but we **digressed** to a discussion of whether Winnie the Pooh has a telephone.

4 **incentive**
(in-sen'-tiv)
-noun

  a. "As an **incentive** to call now," said the TV salesman, "the first 500 callers will receive this genuine imitation-leather handbag!"

  b. The thought of myself in a bathing suit next summer provides me with adequate **incentive** to exercise.

5 **incorporate**
(in-kôr'-pər-āt')
-verb

  a. Jerry **incorporated** all of his favorite desserts into one: a chocolate-covered banana-cream pecan pie.

  b. Since the number of young children has gone down in my neighborhood, the two elementary schools have been **incorporated** into one.

6 **indispensable**
(in'-di-spen'-sə-bəl)
-adjective

  a. Because there's no bus or train service nearby, a car is **indispensable** in my neighborhood.

  b. When you're broke, you find that many things you thought were **indispensable** were merely nice to have around.

7 **intermittent**
(in'-tər-mit'-ənt)
-adjective

  a. You have to work steadily with your dog to train him well. **Intermittent** practice won't work.

  b. Dora realized that weight loss would be **intermittent** when she dieted, so she didn't give up when the losses stopped and started.

8 **succumb**
(sə-kum')
-verb

  a. Leah **succumbed** to her daughter's begging and bought her a pet lizard for her birthday.

  b. Once the suspect was arrested, he quickly **succumbed** and confessed to stealing the car stereo.

Matching Words and Definitions

Check your understanding of the eight words by matching each word with its definition. Look back at the sentences in "Eight Words in Context" as needed to decide on the meaning of each word.

_____ 1. **curtail**	a.	to cut short; reduce
_____ 2. **devastate**	b.	something that moves one to take action or work harder; encouragement
_____ 3. **digress**	c.	to turn aside or stray, especially from the main topic in speaking or writing
_____ 4. **incentive**	d.	to upset; disappoint greatly
_____ 5. **incorporate**	e.	to give in; give up resisting
_____ 6. **indispensable**	f.	necessary
_____ 7. **intermittent**	g.	to unite into a single whole; combine
_____ 8. **succumb (to)**	h.	starting and stopping from time to time; off-and-on

CAUTION: Do not go any further until you are sure the above answers are correct. If you have studied the "Eight Words in Context," you will know how to match each word. Then you can use the matches to help you in the following practices. Your goal is to reach a point where you don't need to check definitions at all.

➤ Sentence Check 1

Complete each sentence below with the most suitable word from the box. Use each word once.

curtail	devastate	digress	incentive
incorporate	indispensable	intermittent	succumb

1. _____ rain kept interrupting the ballgame.

2. The sight of her bandaged husband in an oxygen tent _____(e)d Claire.

3. Someone has managed to _____ a tomato and a potato into one plant.

4. A home computer and a telephone are _____ tools for many self-employed people.

5. Airlines offer "frequent flyer credits" toward free trips as _____s to people who fly often.

6. The man on the corner offered to sell me a watch, but he quickly _____(e)d his sales pitch when he saw a police officer approach.

7. Because our history teacher loved to gab, we often could get him to _____ from the lesson to talk about school athletics or school politics.

8. Carl resisted Lola's charms for months, thinking she was too young for him, but he finally

   _____(e)d and asked her out to dinner.

Now check your answers to these questions by turning to page 118. Going over the answers carefully will help you prepare for the next two checks, for which answers are not given.

➤ Sentence Check 2

Complete each sentence below with two words from the box. Use each word once.

curtail	devastate	digress	incentive
incorporate	indispensable	intermittent	succumb

1-2. The company decided to _____ the construction of its new plant until the architects

could decide on how to _____ an employee gym into the new building.

3-4. My aunt has only _____ success in quitting smoking. Every few months she

_____s to temptation, and then she has to quit all over again.

5-6. As Leo explained a failed business deal that once _____(e)d him, he

_____(e)d into the even more interesting tale of his romance with Molly, his business

partner.

7-8. The vitamin saleswoman offered me free samples, 90-day trials, and every other

_____ she could think of to get me to buy. Her sales pitch was so convincing that I

was starting to believe her products were _____ to my well-being.

➤ Final Check: Learning to Study

Here is a final opportunity for you to strengthen your knowledge of the eight words. First read the following passage carefully. Then fill in each blank with a word from the box at the top of this page. (Context clues will help you figure out which word goes in which blank.) Use each word once.

Linda never had to work very hard to make good grades in high school. But it was different in college, where the challenges were greater. It was also much easier in college for Linda to waste time going to parties. She didn't realize how badly she was doing until she saw her mid-term grades, which completely (1)_____(e)d her. She knew she had to make some big changes right away. As a(n) (2)_____ to study more, she tried studying with her friend Denise. But that didn't work; their conversation would (3)_____ from European history to personal topics, such as dates or favorite singers.

Linda decided she'd have to go it alone. She began to skip weekday parties and also to (4)_____ the time she spent talking with friends. She discovered that finding a good place to study was (5)_____ to her new study habits. In the silence of the library's third floor, there were no temptations to which she could (6)_____. At first, the improvement in Linda's grades was only (7)_____—A's and B's alternated with C's and D's. But little by little, she learned to (8)_____ a social life with serious study and get grades she was proud of.

Previewing the Words

Find out how many of the eight words in this chapter you already know. Try to complete each sentence with the most suitable word from the list below. Use each word once.

Leave a sentence blank rather than guessing at an answer. Your purpose here is just to get a sense of the eight words and what you may know about them.

alleviate	benefactor	covert	infamous
intrinsic	revulsion	speculate	virile

1. I took some aspirin to _____ my pounding headache.

2. Lassie has the qualities of loyalty and affection that seem _____ to all dogs.

3. The wealthy _____ who paid for the child's kidney operation prefers to remain anonymous.

4. Filled with _____ by all the killings, I walked out in the middle of the horror movie.

5. Typhoid Mary is _____ for knowingly spreading typhoid by taking jobs that involved working with food.

6. The therapist asked Cassy to _____ on what might happen if she told Ralph her true feelings.

7. My brother likes to wear sleeveless "muscle shirts." He thinks they make him look more

_____.

8. The public knew the woman as an international business leader. Only a few CIA officials knew her

_____ role as an international spy.

Now check your answers by turning to page 118. Fix any mistakes and fill in any blank spaces by writing in the correct answers. By doing so, you will complete this introduction to the eight words.

You're now ready to strengthen your knowledge of the words you already know and to master the words you're only half sure of, or don't know at all. Turn to the next page.

Eight Words in Context

Figure out the meanings of the following eight words by looking *closely and carefully* at the context in which the words appear. Doing so will prepare you for the matching test and practices on the two pages that follow.

1 **alleviate**
(ə-lē'-vē-āt')
-*verb*

    a. To **alleviate** his loneliness, the widower moved closer to his daughter and her family.

    b. After a long game in the August heat, the young baseball players **alleviated** their thirst with ice-cold lemonade.

2 **benefactor**
(ben'-ə-fak'-tər)
-*noun*

    a. The Second Street Bank is a long-time **benefactor** of the arts. This year it will sponsor a series of free jazz concerts in the parks.

    b. Many famous composers, including Mozart, would not have been able to compose very much without the financial support of royal **benefactors**.

3 **covert**
(kuv'-ərt)
-*adjective*

    a. Miriam and David's relationship is so **covert** that they never eat out. Even Miriam's parents don't know she is seeing him.

    b. If you enjoy **covert** activities, become a secret agent.

4 **infamous**
(in'-fə-məs)
-*adjective*

    a. King Henry VIII of England was **infamous** for executing two of his six wives.

    b. Visitors to the dungeons of ancient castles always want to see the instruments of torture, including the **infamous** Iron Maiden—a body-shaped box with spikes inside.

5 **intrinsic**
(in-trin'-sik)
-*adjective*

    a. Trust is **intrinsic** to any good friendship.

    b. Because Lian has an **intrinsic** desire to learn, she doesn't need the reward of good grades to motivate her studies.

6 **revulsion**
(ri-vul'-shən)
-*noun*

    a. Whenever I read about child abuse in the newspaper, I am filled with such **revulsion** that I often cannot finish the article.

    b. When Sharon met the man who had cheated her father, she was overcome with **revulsion**.

7 **speculate**
(spek'-yə-lāt')
-*verb*

    a. It's interesting to **speculate** how history might have been different if Abraham Lincoln had lived a few years longer.

    b. Scientists **speculate** that the reason birds don't give birth to live young is that a bird's high body heat would harm a developing fetus.

8 **virile**
(vîr'-əl)
-*adjective*

    a. Men who are unsure about their masculinity sometimes try to "prove" they are **virile** by being overly aggressive.

    b. When a male heron stamps his feet and sticks his neck out, and then drops his head and says "plop-buzz," the female finds him very **virile**. In fact, that behavior is how the male attracts a mate.

Matching Words and Definitions

Check your understanding of the eight words by matching each word with its definition. Look back at the sentences in "Eight Words in Context" as needed to decide on the meaning of each word.

_____ 1. **alleviate**

_____ 2. **benefactor**

_____ 3. **covert**

_____ 4. **infamous**

_____ 5. **intrinsic**

_____ 6. **revulsion**

_____ 7. **speculate**

_____ 8. **virile**

a. secret; hidden

b. belonging to a person or thing by its very nature (and thus not dependent on circumstances)

c. having a very bad reputation; widely known for being vicious, criminal, or deserving of contempt

d. a person or organization that gives help, especially financial aid

e. manly; masculine

f. to come up with ideas or theories about a subject; theorize

g. to relieve; make easier to bear

h. great disgust or distaste

CAUTION: Do not go any further until you are sure the above answers are correct. If you have studied the "Eight Words in Context," you will know how to match each word. Then you can use the matches to help you in the following practices. Your goal is to reach a point where you don't need to check definitions at all.

➤*Sentence Check 1*

Complete each sentence below with the most suitable word from the box. Use each word once.

alleviate	benefactor	covert	infamous
intrinsic	revulsion	speculate	virile

1. Problems are _____ to life; they're unavoidable.

2. My hunger isn't fully satisfied, but the apple _____(e)d it somewhat.

3. Teenage guys usually welcome a deepening voice and a thickening beard as signs they are becoming more

   _____.

4. Though she was tried and found not guilty, Lizzie Borden is still _____ for killing her parents with a hatchet.

5. The children loved the _____ activities involved in preparing their mother's surprise party.

6. The mass murderer's neighbors were overcome with _____ when they learned what their "friend" had been doing in his basement.

7. "As no group has claimed responsibility, we can only _____ on the motives for the bombing," said the newscaster.

8. Roger Novak had been a well-known _____ of AIDS research, so it was no surprise that he left a lot of money for the research in his will.

Now check your answers to these questions by turning to page 118. Going over the answers carefully will help you prepare for the next two checks, for which answers are not given.

➤ Sentence Check 2

Complete each sentence below with two words from the box. Use each word once.

alleviate	benefactor	covert	infamous
intrinsic	revulsion	speculate	virile

1-2. Nursing is a good career for Dee because it's a(n) _____ part of her personality to try

to _____ people's pain.

3-4. Although everything about the Nazis filled the Dutch spy with _____, his

_____ assignment was to make friends with top Nazi scientists.

5-6. Young men who are bullies usually think of themselves as_____, but a

_____ of the weak is far more manly than someone who takes advantage of weakness.

7-8. With all the wild stories told about Jesse James, the Dalton Gang and other _____

figures of the Wild West, we can only _____ as to how much is fact and how much is

fiction.

➤ Final Check: The Mad Monk

Here is a final opportunity for you to strengthen your knowledge of the eight words. First read the following
passage carefully. Then fill in each blank with a word from the box at the top of this page. (Context clues will
help you figure out which word goes in which blank.) Use each word once.

Shortly before the Russian Revolution, a man named Rasputin became (1)_____ as the
"mad monk." Because he dressed like a peasant, drank heavily, and rarely bathed, the nobility often felt
(2)_____ when they first met him.

Yet despite his outward appearance, Rasputin possessed a(n) (3)_____ charm that
drew many to him, including the Russian Empress. She thought him a great man of God and a special
(4)_____ to her seriously ill son, whose condition she felt Rasputin (5)_____d.

However, many thought Rasputin was concerned only with his own power and pleasure. Some critics
even dared to (6)_____ that the monk and the Empress were romantically involved. This
theory was strengthened by the fact that the Empress's "holy man" pursued many women and boasted about
how (7)_____ he was.

Finally, a group of Russian noblemen made (8)_____ plans to kill Rasputin.
Somehow, the secret must have gotten out, for a Russian official warned Rasputin of a plot against him. He
nevertheless accepted the noblemen's invitation to a dinner party, where they served him poisoned wine and
cake. When Rasputin seemed unaffected by the poison, his enemies shot him, then stabbed him, and finally
dumped him into an icy river. An autopsy revealed that he had died by drowning.

SCORES: Sentence Check 2 _____ %   Final Check _____ %
Enter your scores above and in the vocabulary performance chart on the inside back cover of the book.

Number right: 8 = 100%   7 = 88%   6 = 75%   5 = 63%   4 = 50%   3 = 38%   2 = 25%   1 = 13%

UNIT TWO: Test 1

PART A
Choose the word that best completes each sentence and write it in the space provided.

1. **digress**
   speculate
   curtail
   confiscate

   Scientists _____ that the average life span of a dinosaur

   was probably 100 to 120 years.

2. **retaliate**
   degenerate
   confiscate
   decipher

   Unless figure skaters practice regularly, their skills will _____.

3. **implausible**
   blatant
   covert
   virile

   It may sound _____, but a camel can drink twenty-five

   gallons of water.

4. **immaculate**
   infamous
   incoherent
   concurrent

   Movie subtitles should be _____ with the spoken words they

   are translating.

5. **sinister**
   immaculate
   incoherent
   intricate

   Even the most _____ people have microscopic creatures

   clinging to their hair.

6. **blight**
   plagiarism
   qualm
   prerequisite

   Measles remains a serious _____ worldwide, killing over a

   million people each year.

7. **deciphered**
   retaliated
   curtailed
   speculated

   A power failure _____ our viewing of the TV mystery, so

   we never found out who had committed the murder.

8. **suffice**
   alleviate
   constitute
   default

   The government student loan program is in serious trouble because many

   students _____ on their payments.

9. **blatant**
   virile
   covert
   immaculate

   The CIA's _____ activities often include "bugging" people's

   telephone lines with tiny, hidden microphones.

10. **vulnerable**
    nominal
    incoherent
    sinister

    Although our college library charges only a(n) _____ fee to

    use a typewriter or computer, I don't think it should charge students any fee at

    all.

(Continues on next page)

53

PART B
Circle **C** if the italicized word is used **correctly**. Circle **I** if the word is used **incorrectly.**

C I 11. Our English teacher said, "Be sure to *digress*. A short essay needs a tight focus."

C I 12. Ocean plants *constitute* about 85 percent of all the greenery on Earth.

C I 13. Jesse Jackson is often praised for his *garbled* speeches.

C I 14. The beautiful sunset, with dramatic red swirls in a pink sky, filled us with *revulsion*.

C I 15. Elise enjoys *intricate* jigsaw puzzles, such as those of detailed flower displays.

C I 16. Vince *gloated* when he learned his girlfriend was moving to another state.

C I 17. A *prerequisite* for getting the health insurance policy is a satisfactory exam by a company physician.

C I 18. Adult dolphins often form a protective ring around young ones to keep them *vulnerable* from attack.

C I 19. Felix's teacher suspected him of *plagiarism* because his last paper was written so much better than his others.

C I 20. In a *blatant* case of injustice, a wealthy and influential North Carolina man received no punishment when he was caught selling cocaine.

SCORE: (Number correct) _____ x 5 = _____ %

Enter your scores above and in the vocabulary performance chart on the inside back cover of the book.

UNIT TWO: *Test 2*

PART A

Complete each sentence with a word from the box. Use each word once.

alleviate	benefactor	confiscate	decipher	intermittent
qualm	retaliate	sinister	succumb	suffice

1. In irregular bursts of energy, dying stars give off _____ radio signals.

2. The muscle ointment will _____ the pain of your sprained neck.

3. The owner of the restaurant decided to _____ to public pressure and establish a non-smoking section.

4. A hint to my daughter to take out the garbage won't _____. She needs to be told to do so.

5. I don't know who sent me the birthday card because I couldn't _____ the signature.

6. The Russian Communists, who opposed private wealth, _____(e)d the property of wealthy landowners.

7. Through the years, people with _____s about having cheated on their income taxes have sent gifts of money to the IRS.

8. The Rumanian people _____(e)d against their Communist dictator, who had ordered mass murders, by executing him.

9. The high school's chief _____ has offered to pay all college costs for any low-income student who graduates from high school.

10. One of the oddest _____ plots of all time was the one thought up by a wealthy Frenchman. He fed his victims rich foods until they died of overeating.

(Continues on next page)

PART B
Circle **C** if the italicized word is used **correctly.** Circle **I** if the word is used **incorrectly.**

C   I   11.   Finally getting the raise she had hoped for *devastated* Jill.

C   I   12.   A typewriter or word processor is *indispensable* for preparing a college term paper.

C   I   13.   Since baldness is a masculine trait, why don't more men view it as attractively *virile?*

C   I   14.   President Harry S. Truman was *infamous* for the sign on his desk that read "The buck stops here."

C   I   15.   I don't consider retirement benefits a sufficient *incentive* to stick with a job I dislike.

C   I   16.   Farm *Sanctuary* offers a safe, comfortable home to farm animals who have been rescued from cruel conditions.

C   I   17.   The Democratic and Republican parties are the main parties in the U.S., but others, such as the Socialist Party, are *predominant.*

C   I   18.   Some critics think Abraham Lincoln was a literary genius because of the powerful, *incoherent* speeches he wrote.

C   I   19.   The desire to aid others seems *intrinsic* to many animals. Baboons, for example, will try to free other baboons who are caged.

C   I   20.   My husband and I *incorporate* all our money into several checking and savings accounts, rather than combine all the money in one account.

SCORE: (Number correct) _____ x 5 = _____ %

Enter your scores above and in the vocabulary performance chart on the inside back cover of the book.

UNIT TWO: Test 3

PART A: Synonyms
In the space provided, write the letter of the choice that is most nearly the **same** in meaning as the boldfaced word.

_____ 1. **sanctuary**   **a)** encouragement   **b)** shelter   **c)** requirement   **d)** decline

_____ 2. **covert**   **a)** necessary   **b)** slight   **c)** natural   **d)** secret

_____ 3. **benefactor**   **a)** hero   **b)** entertainer   **c)** helper   **d)** owner

_____ 4. **alleviate**   **a)** take   **b)** ease   **c)** repay   **d)** build

_____ 5. **intermittent**   **a)** off-and-on   **b)** within   **c)** perfectly clean   **d)** complex

_____ 6. **digress**   **a)** be the parts of   **b)** turn aside   **c)** read   **d)** guess

_____ 7. **plagiarism**   **a)** requirement   **b)** distaste   **c)** failure   **d)** stealing another's writings

_____ 8. **confiscate**   **a)** seize   **b)** interpret   **c)** make up   **d)** waste

_____ 9. **garble**   **a)** respond   **b)** pay back   **c)** relieve   **d)** scramble

_____ 10. **constitute**   **a)** seize   **b)** coexist   **c)** form   **d)** assume

_____ 11. **prerequisite**   **a)** cause   **b)** requirement   **c)** encouragement   **d)** difficulty

_____ 12. **speculate**   **a)** notice   **b)** theorize   **c)** give in to   **d)** combine

_____ 13. **default**   **a)** upset greatly   **b)** plan   **c)** aid   **d)** fail to do something required

_____ 14. **revulsion**   **a)** charm   **b)** disgust   **c)** encouragement   **d)** something that weakens

_____ 15. **decipher**   **a)** interpret   **b)** think up   **c)** relieve   **d)** turn aside

_____ 16. **retaliate**   **a)** follow   **b)** cut short   **c)** pay back   **d)** disappoint greatly

_____ 17. **nominal**   **a)** necessary   **b)** obvious   **c)** evil   **d)** slight

_____ 18. **qualm**   **a)** doubt of conscience   **b)** inspection   **c)** requirement   **d)** demand

_____ 19. **concurrent**   **a)** most noticeable   **b)** complicated   **c)** weak   **d)** existing together

_____ 20. **intrinsic**   **a)** manly   **b)** wicked   **c)** natural   **d)** open to injury

(Continues on next page)

PART B: Antonyms
In the space provided, write the letter of the choice that is most nearly the **opposite** in meaning to the boldfaced word.

____ 21. **immaculate**   a) confused   b) good   c) filthy   d) slight

____ 22. **suffice**   a) plan   b) be insufficient   c) be the whole of   d) give

____ 23. **blight**   a) benefit   b) peace   c) increase   d) friendliness

____ 24. **incentive**   a) improvement   b) mix-up   c) failure   d) discouragement

____ 25. **gloat**   a) express regret   b) misinterpret   c) forget   d) resist

____ 26. **degenerate**   a) command   b) give   c) try   d) improve

____ 27. **indispensable**   a) perfectly clean   b) large   c) protected   d) unnecessary

____ 28. **implausible**   a) common   b) believable   c) righteous   d) inspiring

____ 29. **predominant**   a) uncommon   b) complicated   c) weak   d) early

____ 30. **blatant**   a) serious   b) unnatural   c) unnoticeable   d) beneficial

____ 31. **intricate**   a) encouraging   b) at fault   c) simple   d) unsteady

____ 32. **devastate**   a) comfort   b) educate   c) admit   d) continue

____ 33. **infamous**   a) believable   b) young   c) alive   d) honorably famous

____ 34. **curtail**   a) improve   b) extend   c) admit   d) beautify

____ 35. **incoherent**   a) quiet   b) well-known   c) logical   d) friendly

____ 36. **virile**   a) homely   b) unnatural   c) graceful   d) feminine

____ 37. **succumb**   a) resist   b) attract   c) learn   d) delay

____ 38. **incorporate**   a) separate   b) do openly   c) add to   d) lose

____ 39. **vulnerable**   a) clear   b) right   c) complete   d) protected

____ 40. **sinister**   a) small   b) good   c) humorous   d) simple

SCORE: (Number correct) _____ x 2.5 = _____ %

Enter your scores above and in the vocabulary performance chart on the inside back cover of the book.

UNIT TWO: *Test 4*

PART A
Complete each sentence in a way that clearly shows you understand the meaning of the boldfaced word.
Take a minute to plan your answer before you write.

    Example: As an **incentive** to work better, my boss ____*awards bonuses to workers who show special effort.*

1. One of the more **infamous** people I've heard of is _____

2. I feel **revulsion** when I see _____

_____

3. The reason the plan was **covert** was that _____

_____

4. When Carolyn saw her essay grade, she **gloated**, saying, " _____

_____

5. During the math class, the teacher **digressed** by _____

_____

6. My apartment is so **immaculate** that _____

_____

7. A good friend of mine was once **devastated** by _____

_____

8. The novel's main character is a **sinister** doctor who _____

_____

9. When my neighbor cut lilacs off my bush for her home, I **retaliated** by _____

_____

10. One **prerequisite** for getting married ought to be _____

_____

(Continues on next page)

PART B

After each boldfaced word are a *synonym* (a word that means the same as the boldfaced word), an *antonym* (a word that means the opposite of the boldfaced word), and a word that is neither. Mark the synonym with an *S* and the antonym with an *A*.

	Example: **nominal**	_____ personal	_A_ enormous	_S_ slight
11-12.	**confiscate**	_____ give	_____ seize	_____ combine
13-14.	**alleviate**	_____ relieve	_____ worsen	_____ raise
15-16.	**intricate**	_____ musical	_____ complicated	_____ simple
17-18.	**incorporate**	_____ combine	_____ resist	_____ separate
19-20.	**indispensable**	_____ essential	_____ expensive	_____ unnecessary

PART C

Use five of the following ten words in sentences. Make it clear that you know the meaning of the word you use. Feel free to use the past tense or plural form of a word.

blight	curtail	decipher	implausible	predominant
qualm	sanctuary	speculate	virile	vulnerable

21. _____

_____

22. _____

_____

23. _____

_____

24. _____

_____

25. _____

_____

SCORE: (Number correct) _____ x 4 = _____ %

Enter your scores above and in the vocabulary performance chart on the inside back cover of the book.

Unit Three

Previewing the Words

Find out how many of the eight words in this chapter you already know. Try to complete each sentence with the most suitable word from the list below. Use each word once.

Leave a sentence blank rather than guessing at an answer. Your purpose here is just to get a sense of the eight words and what you may know about them.

abstain	agnostic	aspire	benevolent
deficit	dissent	lucrative	mandatory

1. Muriel is a(n) _____ who prays when she's in trouble, just in case God exists.

2. That computer business is so _____ that its profits rose almost 200 percent last year.

3. After conquering his alcoholism, Michael felt it was safest to _____ from all forms of alcohol, including dinner wine.

4. Millions of young people _____ to be professional athletes, but only a few will succeed.

5. "Since automobile insurance is _____," Dad said, "you have no choice but to pay the high rates."

6. The dictator permitted people to agree with his policies or keep silent about them, but not to

   express _____.

7. When I foolishly overspent last year, I quickly made up the _____ by taking a part-time job for a few months.

8. Henry Burton, in a poem, gave good advice on being _____: "Have you had a kindness shown? Pass it on."

Now check your answers by turning to page 118. Fix any mistakes and fill in any blank spaces by writing in the correct answers. By doing so, you will complete this introduction to the eight words.

You're now ready to strengthen your knowledge of the words you already know and to master the words you're only half sure of, or don't know at all. Turn to the next page.

Eight Words in Context

Figure out the meanings of the following eight words by looking *closely and carefully* at the context in which the words appear. Doing so will prepare you for the matching test and practices on the two pages that follow.

1 **abstain**
(ab-stān')
-*verb*

   a. Although Lou has given up cigarettes, he doesn't **abstain** from tobacco. Now he chews it.

   b. My sister called off her engagement to Clayton because he wouldn't **abstain** from dating other women.

2 **agnostic**
(ag-nos'-tik)
-*noun*

   a. Iris believes there is a God, and Marcia feels sure there isn't. Jean, an **agnostic**, feels that we can't be certain one way or the other.

   b. My uncle, who was an **agnostic**, used to say, "Humans cannot understand a flower, let alone whether or not there's a God."

3 **aspire**
(ə-spīr')
-*verb*

   a. Derek, who loves drawing buildings, **aspires** to be a great architect.

   b. Horatio Nelson, one of history's great naval commanders, **aspired** to a goal he never reached—overcoming his seasickness.

4 **benevolent**
(bə-nev'-ə-lənt)
-*adjective*

   a. My grandmother is one of the most **benevolent** people I know. She's always doing something kind.

   b. In 19th-century London, William Booth founded a **benevolent** association to help the poor, the Salvation Army.

5 **deficit**
(def'-ə-sit)
-*noun*

   a. The U.S. has spent so much more than it has taken in that it now has a huge budget **deficit**.

   b. Residents are asked not to water their lawns because a **deficit** of rain has dangerously lowered the water supply.

6 **dissent**
(di-sent')
-*noun*

   a. The committee was so torn by **dissent** that its members could not even agree on whether or not to schedule another meeting.

   b. There was **dissent** between principals and the school board over whether or not the public schools should be in session all year round.

7 **lucrative**
(loo'-krə-tiv)
-*adjective*

   a. Investments in the stock market can be **lucrative**. However, they can also result in great financial loss.

   b. "Teaching at a small college isn't **lucrative**," Professor Baum admitted, "but I've never felt the need to make lots of money."

8 **mandatory**
(man'-də-tôr'-ē)
-*adjective*

   a. Members of the basketball team have to follow strict rules. For example, it's **mandatory** that each player attend at least 80 percent of the practices.

   b. "A research paper isn't **mandatory**," the instructor said, "but if you write one, you'll get extra credit."

Matching Words and Definitions

Check your understanding of the eight words by matching each word with its definition. Look back at the sentences in "Eight Words in Context" as needed to decide on the meaning of each word.

_____ 1. **abstain (from)**　　a. to strongly desire (a condition or goal); long for something

_____ 2. **agnostic**　　b. profitable; well-paying

_____ 3. **aspire (to)**　　c. a shortage; a lack in amount or quality

_____ 4. **benevolent**　　d. to voluntarily do without; hold oneself back from doing something

_____ 5. **deficit**　　e. kind; charitable

_____ 6. **dissent**　　f. a person who believes we cannot know whether or not there is a God

_____ 7. **lucrative**　　g. required

_____ 8. **mandatory**　　h. disagreement

CAUTION: Do not go any further until you are sure the above answers are correct. If you have studied the "Eight Words in Context," you will know how to match each word. Then you can use the matches to help you in the following practices. Your goal is to reach a point where you don't need to check definitions at all.

➤Sentence Check 1

Complete each sentence below with the most suitable word from the box. Use each word once.

abstain	agnostic	aspire	benevolent
deficit	dissent	lucrative	mandatory

1. The greatest goal to which my kid brother _____s is the Pinball Championship of the World.

2. The _____ fund at my church collects money to help the needy.

3. An entrance fee wasn't _____, but a museum sign suggested that visitors make a donation.

4. Because Hank needs to lose weight, his doctor recommended that he _____ from all sweets and fatty foods.

5. We could overcome a _____ of organs if more people would agree to have their organs transplanted after they die.

6. There was no _____ in the family on whether or not to start a vegetable garden this year. We all agreed it was a great idea.

7. "When someone who believes in God marries someone who does not," the comic asked, "do they give birth to a(n) _____?"

8. Acting is _____ for only a small percentage of performers. The rest need additional sources of income, such as waiting on tables or driving a cab.

Now check your answers to these questions by turning to page 118. Going over the answers carefully will help you prepare for the next two checks, for which answers are not given.

➤Sentence Check 2

Complete each sentence below with two words from the box. Use each word once.

abstain	agnostic	aspire	benevolent
deficit	dissent	lucrative	mandatory

1-2. Gale didn't _____ from smoking cigarettes at the office until her employer made non-smoking _____.

3-4. "Although I'm a(n) _____," said Stan, "I still hope that there's a God who's _____ and loving."

5-6. The _____ in the township treasury is causing a lot of _____ over whether or not taxes should be raised.

7-8. Because my father _____s to make enough money to send his children to college, he's working hard to make his auto repair business as _____ as possible.

➤Final Check: Conflict over Holidays

Here is a final opportunity for you to strengthen your knowledge of the eight words. First read the following passage carefully. Then fill in each blank with a word from the box at the top of this page. (Context clues will help you figure out which word goes in which blank.) Use each word once.

While Jeanne and Paul are generally a happily married couple, they do struggle over one point of (1)_____. They disagree as to how their family should observe religious holidays. Jeanne feels that the emphasis on holiday presents and parties has made the season (2)_____ to merchants while leaving an unnecessarily large (3)_____ in people's budgets. She complains that exchanging presents at Christmas is practically (4)_____, whether or not one believes in the holiday's religious significance. Jeanne (5)_____s to keep her home free of all such nonreligious customs and thus wants her children to (6)_____ from traditions such as gift-giving and dyeing Easter eggs. She feels the family's money would be better spent if it were donated to a (7)_____ organization for helping the poor. Some of Jeanne's neighbors assume that she is a(n) (8)_____ because of her lack of holiday spirit. They are wrong, however. Jeanne believes deeply in God. While Paul understands Jeanne's concerns, he enjoys the holiday traditions such as visits to Santa Claus and Easter egg hunts. He sees them as pleasant customs that add to the joy of the year.

SCORES: **Sentence Check 2** _____ %   **Final Check** _____ %
Enter your scores above and in the vocabulary performance chart on the inside back cover of the book.

Number right: 8 = 100%   7 = 88%   6 = 75%   5 = 63%   4 = 50%   3 = 38%   2 = 25%   1 = 13%

Previewing the Words

Find out how many of the eight words in this chapter you already know. Try to complete each sentence with the most suitable word from the list below. Use each word once.

Leave a sentence blank rather than guessing at an answer. Your purpose here is just to get a sense of the eight words and what you may know about them.

charisma	contemporary	conversely	extrovert
prevalent	proponent	quest	traumatic

1. Fear was _____ throughout the town until the escaped murderer was captured and put safely behind bars.

2. Beth likes _____ furniture, but her husband prefers older styles.

3. Many scientists worldwide are active in the _____ for a cure for cancer.

4. My sister thinks that being an attorney is an exciting career. _____, I believe that most of a lawyer's work is dry and boring.

5. Lucy has such _____ that when she ran for class president, almost every person in the tenth grade voted for her.

6. Getting lost in the subway when I was only five years old was a(n) _____ experience. Even now, it upsets me to recall the event.

7. Arnie is a(n) _____ of the Equal Rights Amendment. He believes the law should give women the same rights as men.

8. "I wish I were more of a(n) _____," Miko told her counselor. "I'm so shy that sometimes I can barely talk to people."

Now check your answers by turning to page 118. Fix any mistakes and fill in any blank spaces by writing in the correct answers. By doing so, you will complete this introduction to the eight words.

You're now ready to strengthen your knowledge of the words you already know and to master the words you're only half sure of, or don't know at all. Turn to the next page.

Eight Words in Context

Figure out the meanings of the following eight words by looking *closely and carefully* at the context in which the words appear. Doing so will prepare you for the matching test and practices on the two pages that follow.

1 **charisma**
(kə-riz'-mə)
-*noun*

   a. John Kennedy's **charisma**, perhaps even more than his policies, brought him widespread support.

   b. Her numerous loyal fans worldwide show that Great Britain's Princess Diana certainly has **charisma**.

2 **contemporary**
(kən-tem'-pə-rer'-ē)
-*adjective*

   a. I prefer "golden oldie" movies to most **contemporary** films.

   b. My grandfather says that compared to kids in his day, **contemporary** youth are soft and lazy.

3 **conversely**
(kən-vûrs'-lē)
-*adverb*

   a. Ron, who is basically bored by food, eats in order to live. **Conversely**, Nate so loves food that he seems to live in order to eat.

   b. Mary drives her children to school whenever it rains. **Conversely**, I make my kids walk as usual because I think a little rain never hurt anyone.

4 **extrovert**
(ek'-strə-vûrt')
-*noun*

   a. Surprisingly, not all performers are **extroverts**. When offstage, many are quiet and shy.

   b. My boss was looking for someone to greet and chat with her clients, so I recommended Robert for the job because he's such an **extrovert**.

5 **prevalent**
(prev'-ə-lənt)
-*adjective*

   a. Unemployment was **prevalent** during America's Great Depression. By 1932, over 12 million people were out of work.

   b. Television sets are more **prevalent** in the U.S. than bathtubs. Over half of American homes have two or more TV's. Far fewer homes have more than one bathtub.

6 **proponent**
(prō-pō'-nənt)
-*noun*

   a. I voted for Senator Williams, a **proponent** of improved services for the elderly, because I feel many older people need greater assistance.

   b. Elaine is a **proponent** of employer-supported day care. She believes every big company should help provide care for its workers' children.

7 **quest**
(kwest)
-*noun*

   a. During Carlos' **quest** for the perfect pizza, he sampled the cheese pizza at twenty-seven different restaurants.

   b. Ponce de Leon's **quest** was for the Fountain of Youth; what he found instead was Florida.

8 **traumatic**
(trô-mat'-ik)
-*adjective*

   a. Divorce can be less **traumatic** for children if their fears and feelings are taken into account as the divorce takes place.

   b. My cousin has had nightmares ever since his **traumatic** experience of being trapped in a coal mine.

Matching Words and Definitions

Check your understanding of the eight words by matching each word with its definition. Look back at the sentences in "Eight Words in Context" as needed to decide on the meaning of each word.

_____	1. **charisma**	a. in a reversed way; in an opposite or contrary manner
_____	2. **contemporary**	b. the quality of a leader which captures great popular devotion; personal magnetism; charm
_____	3. **conversely**	c. a search; hunt
_____	4. **extrovert**	d. widespread; common
_____	5. **prevalent**	e. modern; up-to-date
_____	6. **proponent (of)**	f. someone who supports a cause
_____	7. **quest**	g. causing painful emotions, with possible long-lasting psychological effects
_____	8. **traumatic**	h. an outgoing, expressive person

CAUTION: Do not go any further until you are sure the above answers are correct. If you have studied the "Eight Words in Context," you will know how to match each word. Then you can use the matches to help you in the following practices. Your goal is to reach a point where you don't need to check definitions at all.

➤ Sentence Check 1

Complete each sentence below with the most suitable word from the box. Use each word once.

charisma	contemporary	conversely	extrovert
prevalent	proponent	quest	traumatic

1. I study best in the morning. _____, my sister concentrates better at night.

2. Nancy is a(n) _____ by nature, but since she's become depressed, she has been avoiding other people.

3. Underage drinking was so _____ in the fraternity house that college officials ordered the house closed for a year.

4. Neal is a(n) _____ of exercising for good health. He even encourages his young children to swim or cycle every day.

5. Although some movie stars are short on talent, they have a(n) _____ that makes people want to see their films.

6. Abby didn't like the apartment with the old-fashioned tub and radiators. She preferred a more

   _____ place.

7. Repeating third grade was _____ for my brother. It still pains him to think about it, even though he's a successful businessman now.

8. In the past 300 years, several people have gone on a(n) _____ for Noah's Ark. Some have looked for it in northwestern Turkey, on Mount Ararat, 16,000 feet above sea level.

Now check your answers to these questions by turning to page 118. Going over the answers carefully will help you prepare for the next two checks, for which answers are not given.

➤ *Sentence Check 2*

Complete each sentence below with two words from the box. Use each word once.

charisma	contemporary	conversely	extrovert
prevalent	proponent	quest	traumatic

1-2. Many people are surprised to learn how _____ poverty is in _____ America. Today, millions live below the poverty line.

3-4. A(n) _____, Judy chooses work that brings her in heavy contact with others. _____, Marty prefers jobs in which he mainly works alone.

5-6. Ever since the _____ experience of finding her 12-year-old son dead from a drug overdose, Sophie has been a strong _____ of drug education for all ages.

7-8. Mahatma Gandhi's _____ and vision inspired millions of fellow Indians to join him enthusiastically in the _____ for peaceful solutions to national problems.

➤ *Final Check:* Dr. Martin Luther King, Jr.

Here is a final opportunity for you to strengthen your knowledge of the eight words. First read the following passage carefully. Then fill in each blank with a word from the box at the top of this page. (Context clues will help you figure out which word goes in which blank.) Use each word once.

(1)_____ youth may be able to list the many accomplishments of the Reverend Dr. Martin Luther King, Jr. They may know he was a civil-rights leader who was a(n) (2)_____ of peaceful but direct action. They may know he fought the discrimination against blacks that was more (3)_____ in our country in the 1950's and 1960's. They may also know he was the founder of the Southern Christian Leadership Conference and that he won a Nobel Peace Prize.

But can the young really know the (4)_____, the powerful personal magnetism of this man? When Dr. King spoke, people listened. The warmth of his voice reflected the outwardly directed energy of the (5)_____. Those who heard him felt his message deep within. For most, this meant a stronger belief in and respect for the man and his ideals. (6)_____, for bigots, it meant a hatred and fear of what he stood for.

Dr. King's (7)_____ for equal rights for all was clear when he said, "I have a dream that this nation will rise up and live out the true meaning of its creed: 'We hold these truths to be self-evident; that all men are created equal.'" He gave his time, leadership, and, in the end, his life. His murder was a(n) (8)_____ event in the lives of many Americans, who will never fully recover from that awful day. But because of Martin Luther King, Americans live with greater dignity. And many have taken up his fight for the betterment of all.

SCORES: Sentence Check 2 _____ %   Final Check _____ %

Enter your scores above and in the vocabulary performance chart on the inside back cover of the book.

Number right: 8 = 100%   7 = 88%   6 = 75%   5 = 63%   4 = 50%   3 = 38%   2 = 25%   1 = 13%

Previewing the Words

Find out how many of the eight words in this chapter you already know. Try to complete each sentence with the most suitable word from the list below. Use each word once.

Leave a sentence blank rather than guessing at an answer. Your purpose here is just to get a sense of the eight words and what you may know about them.

congenial	flippant	impasse	perception
prompt	prone	rapport	rationale

1. My sister is more _____ to complaining about her homework than to simply doing it and getting it over with.

2. Our coworkers are very _____ except for Walter, who has remained cool and unfriendly towards everyone.

3. The mountain climbers panicked when they reached a(n) _____. They couldn't go up any farther, but they couldn't go back down either.

4. When asked to explain the _____ behind his decision to divorce, Ed had two strong reasons—his wife's two affairs.

5. Don's boss knows more about business than he does about people. His _____s of his staff's thoughts and feelings are often inaccurate.

6. Many companies _____ people to buy their products by giving them money-saving coupons.

7. When, for the third time, I told my son to clean his room, he gave this _____ response: "Why should I? I just cleaned it last month."

8. Since Barbara broke up with her fiance last year, she has had a hard time developing a(n)

   _____ with other men. She's afraid to get close again.

Now check your answers by turning to page 118. Fix any mistakes and fill in any blank spaces by writing in the correct answers. By doing so, you will complete this introduction to the eight words.

You're now ready to strengthen your knowledge of the words you already know and to master the words you're only half sure of, or don't know at all. Turn to the next page.

Eight Words in Context

Figure out the meanings of the following eight words by looking *closely and carefully* at the context in which the words appear. Doing so will prepare you for the matching test and practices on the two pages that follow.

1 **congenial**
(kən-jēn'-yəl)
-*adjective*

a. You don't find Anita to be **congenial**, but she's pleasant and friendly with me.

b. I was nervous being at a party where I didn't know anyone, but the other guests were so **congenial** that I soon felt at ease.

2 **flippant**
(flip'-ənt)
-*adjective*

a. "Don't give me a **flippant** answer," George's father told him. "Your financial situation is a serious matter."

b. Kim stayed after school a half hour for not bringing her homework and another half hour for her **flippant** excuse—"My goldfish ate it."

3 **impasse**
(im'-pas)
-*noun*

a. The jurors had reached an **impasse**. No decision could be reached because some thought the defendant was the murderer and others were sure he was innocent.

b. If you think you've reached an **impasse** when trying to solve a problem, take a break. After a while, you might think of a solution.

4 **perception**
(pər-sep'-shən)
-*noun*

a. Brenda's **perceptions** of others are usually accurate. She is able to size people up quickly.

b. Our **perceptions** of the problem differ. Rob thinks money is the main issue, but I believe it's a question of who controls the purse strings.

5 **prompt**
(prompt)
-*verb*

a. To **prompt** Byron to get a job, I put the want ads under his pillow.

b. Fast-food clerks **prompt** customers to buy more by asking such questions as "Would you like cookies or apple pie with that?"

6 **prone**
(prōn)
-*adjective*

a. Mr. Walker is **prone** to high blood pressure, so he limits his salt intake.

b. **Prone** to fits of laughter during class, Chris sometimes controls the sound by biting into his pen.

7 **rapport**
(ra-pôr')
-*noun*

a. In high school, I had such good **rapport** with my gym teacher that our close relationship continues to this day.

b. If no **rapport** develops between you and your therapist after a month or two, start looking for another counselor who makes you feel comfortable.

8 **rationale**
(rash'-ə-nal')
-*noun*

a. Danielle's **rationale** for majoring in business was simple. "I want to make a lot of money," she said.

b. The **rationale** for raising the drinking age to 21 is that self-control and good judgment generally increase with age.

Matching Words and Definitions

Check your understanding of the eight words by matching each word with its definition. Look back at the sentences in "Eight Words in Context" as needed to decide on the meaning of each word.

_____ 1. **congenial**   a. an impression; the way someone or something is viewed

_____ 2. **flippant**   b. having a tendency; inclined

_____ 3. **impasse**   c. the underlying reasons for something; logical basis

_____ 4. **perception**   d. disrespectful and not serious enough

_____ 5. **prompt**   e. agreeable or pleasant in character

_____ 6. **prone (to)**   f. to urge into action

_____ 7. **rapport**   g. a situation with no way out; dead end

_____ 8. **rationale**   h. a relationship, especially a close, trusting, or sympathetic one

CAUTION: Do not go any further until you are sure the above answers are correct. If you have studied the "Eight Words in Context," you will know how to match each word. Then you can use the matches to help you in the following practices. Your goal is to reach a point where you don't need to check definitions at all.

➤Sentence Check 1

Complete each sentence below with the most suitable word from the box. Use each word once.

congenial	flippant	impasse	perception
prompt	prone	rapport	rationale

1. Nan is _____ to accidents, so her car insurance rates are quite high.

2. You will get along better in life if you are usually _____, rather than unpleasant.

3. My brother hides his lack of confidence by being _____. He rarely treats anything seriously.

4. It took a magazine article about women who help handicapped children to _____ me to do the same.

5. There was an instant _____ between Duke and Otis. They talked as if they'd known each other for years.

6. At the movie's climax, the bad guys reached a(n) _____. On one side of them was the police; on the other was a tiger.

7. Floyd's _____ of human nature is strongly colored by some bad experiences. He thinks everyone is basically selfish.

8. The _____ behind encouraging pregnant women to gain about twenty-five pounds is that low weight gain can lead to dangerously low birth weights.

Now check your answers to these questions by turning to page 118. Going over the answers carefully will help you prepare for the next two checks, for which answers are not given.

➣ Sentence Check 2

Complete each sentence below with two words from the box. Use each word once.

congenial	flippant	impasse	perception
prompt	prone	rapport	rationale

1-2. Wade is so _____, so easy to talk to, that we established a warm

_____ the first day we met.

3-4. _____ to anger, my mother was quick to punish any of her children who spoke to her

in a _____ way.

5-6. Although the company president explained the _____ behind the pay cuts, his

announcement _____(e)d an employee protest.

7-8. My _____ of the situation is that talks between the factory management and union

officials reached a(n) _____ because neither side would compromise on salaries.

➤ Final Check: Relating to Parents

Here is a final opportunity for you to strengthen your knowledge of the eight words. First read the following passage carefully. Then fill in each blank with a word from the box at the top of this page. (Context clues will help you figure out which word goes in which blank.) Use each word once.

How do you respond when your parents deny you permission to do something? For example, if you want to travel and work around the country for the summer but your parents say you're too young, do you yell and demand your rights? Do you vow to ruin their summer because they've ruined yours? Or do you explain the (1)_____ behind your request, so that your parents will understand your reasoning?

The way you behave when you and your parents reach a(n) (2)_____ on an issue can have a big effect on how they view you. Sure, you could say, "Fine. Just fine. I'll go buy a leash so you can really run my life." But if you are consistently (3)_____ like that, you'll just strengthen their (4)_____ of you as too immature to be on your own. Also, if you ask 300 times a day, "But WHY won't you let me go?" they may tell you where to go, and it won't be on a cross-country trip.

Instead, approach your parents in a (5)_____ way and try to develop a strong, friendly (6)_____ with them. A warm relationship will make them much more (7)_____ to see things your way. Even if you can't (8)_____ them to change their minds about this summer's plans, your chances will be better the next time you want to try something new.

SCORES: Sentence Check 2 _____ %   **Final Check** _____ %

Enter your scores above and in the vocabulary performance chart on the inside back cover of the book.

Number right: 8 = 100%   7 = 88%   6 = 75%   5 = 63%   4 = 50%   3 = 38%   2 = 25%   1 = 13%

Previewing the Words

Find out how many of the eight words in this chapter you already know. Try to complete each sentence with the most suitable word from the list below. Use each word once.

Leave a sentence blank rather than guessing at an answer. Your purpose here is just to get a sense of the eight words and what you may know about them.

averse	detract	divulge	elation
endow	expulsion	nullify	ominous

1. It's against the law to ask people to _____ their age at a job interview.

2. The enormous amount of makeup that Sara wears _____s from her natural beauty.

3. Although Gene was overjoyed and proud to have won the Senate race, he was too tired to show

   _____.

4. One student faces permanent _____ from high school for continually stealing from other people's lockers.

5. My little brother used to be _____ to any foreign food, but now he enjoys Chinese, Indian, and African dishes.

6. A soft drink company decided to _____ its contract with a well-known athlete because he was arrested for drunk driving.

7. One of my classmates is _____(e)d with such musical talent that at six she could hear a tune once and then play it on the piano.

8. The horror movie opened with a view of a(n) _____ old house. Its dark shadows and location high on a cliff seemed to warn of some evil to come.

Now check your answers by turning to page 118. Fix any mistakes and fill in any blank spaces by writing in the correct answers. By doing so, you will complete this introduction to the eight words.

You're now ready to strengthen your knowledge of the words you already know and to master the words you're only half sure of, or don't know at all. Turn to the next page.

Eight Words in Context

Figure out the meanings of the following eight words by looking *closely and carefully* at the context in which the words appear. Doing so will prepare you for the matching test and practices on the two pages that follow.

1 **averse**
(ə-vûrs')
-adjective

    a. My son was once so **averse** to tomatoes that the very sight of them made him gag.

    b. Being **averse** to screaming crowds, I'd rather stay home and listen to a record than go to a rock concert.

2 **detract**
(di-trakt')
-verb

    a. Julius thinks the scar on his cheek **detracts** from his good looks, but it's barely noticeable.

    b. All of the litter in the park certainly **detracts** from the beauty of the trees and flowers.

3 **divulge**
(di-vulj')
-verb

    a. My father wouldn't **divulge** the type of car he had bought, saying only, "It's a surprise."

    b. Unaware that his hairpiece is obvious, Ted has never **divulged** that he's bald, even to his closest friends.

4 **elation**
(i-lā'-shən)
-noun

    a. The principal shouted with **elation** when the school team scored the winning touchdown.

    b. Roy had expected to feel **elation** at his graduation. Instead, he felt sadness at the thought of parting with some of his high school friends.

5 **endow**
(en-dou')
-verb

    a. Nature has **endowed** hummingbirds with the ability to fly backward.

    b. Oscar Wilde was **endowed** with the ability to find humor in any situation. While dying, he said of the ugly wallpaper in his hotel room, "One of us had to go."

6 **expulsion**
(eks-pul'-shən)
-noun

    a. The theater manager told us we risked **expulsion** from the theater if we continued to talk during the movie.

    b. **Expulsion** from school is intended as a punishment, but some students may consider not having to attend classes to be a reward.

7 **nullify**
(nul'-ə-fī')
-verb

    a. The college will **nullify** my student ID at the end of the term unless I update it with a new sticker.

    b. The dead woman's will was **nullified** when her daughter proved that the signature on it had been faked by the woman's lover.

8 **ominous**
(om'-ə-nəs)
-adjective

    a. To many, cemeteries have an **ominous** quality, particularly at night or on Halloween, when the threat of ghosts seems very real.

    b. The sore's failure to heal was **ominous**, a possible sign of cancer.

Matching Words and Definitions

Check your understanding of the eight words by matching each word with its definition. Look back at the sentences in "Eight Words in Context" as needed to decide on the meaning of each word.

_____	1. **averse (to)**	a. to provide with a talent or quality
_____	2. **detract (from)**	b. the act or condition of being dismissed or sent away
_____	3. **divulge·**	c. threatening evil or harm; menacing
_____	4. **elation**	d. to reveal; make known
_____	5. **endow**	e. having a feeling of dislike or distaste for something, thus tending to avoid it
_____	6. **expulsion**	f. to lessen what is admirable or worthwhile about something
_____	7. **nullify**	g. a feeling of great joy or pride
_____	8. **ominous**	h. to make legally ineffective; cancel

CAUTION: Do not go any further until you are sure the above answers are correct. If you have studied the "Eight Words in Context," you will know how to match each word. Then you can use the matches to help you in the following practices. Your goal is to reach a point where you don't need to check definitions at all.

➤ Sentence Check 1

Complete each sentence below with the most suitable word from the box. Use each word once.

averse	detract	divulge	elation
endow	expulsion	nullified	ominous

1. People talking in a movie theater greatly _____ from the experience of watching a film.

2. I'm _____ to speaking in public since I don't enjoy making a fool of myself.

3. When he received the college scholarship, my brother felt such _____ that he wept with joy.

4. The results of the mayor's election were _____ after the townspeople found evidence of voting fraud.

5. The American water shrew is _____(e)d with feet that have air pockets, enabling the small animal to walk on water.

6. Some want a law calling for the _____ of illegal immigrants. Others want all immigrants to be allowed to stay in the U.S.

7. Because of the dark, _____ storm clouds, we cancelled the softball game.

8. Labels on American foods must list the product's ingredients, but many other countries don't require that a product's contents be _____(e)d.

Now check your answers to these questions by turning to page 118. Going over the answers carefully will help you prepare for the next two checks, for which answers are not given.

➤ Sentence Check 2

Complete each sentence below with two words from the following list. Use each word once.

averse	detract	divulge	elation
endow	expulsion	nullified	ominous

1-2.   Some people are so _____ to living near a nuclear plant that they want the the plant's

   license to be _____.

3-4.   Shannon is _____(e)d with beautiful curly red hair, but her self-image is so low that

   she feels her hair _____s from her looks.

5-6.   When someone _____(e)d to college officials that a certain student was selling drugs,

   an investigation began that led to that student's _____ from college.

7-8.   Marty had believed his headaches and blurred vision were _____ signs of some

   terrible disease, so he felt _____ when he learned that he simply needed glasses.

➤ Final Check: The Nightmare of Gym

Here is a final opportunity for you to strengthen your knowledge of the eight words. First read the following passage carefully. Then fill in each blank with a word from the box at the top of this page. (Context clues will help you figure out which word goes in which blank.) Use each word once.

   I was not (1)_____(e)d with athletic ability. In a frequent nightmare, I'm still trying to pass gym so that I can graduate from high school. The situation always looks grim. For one thing, the teacher has threatened me with (2)_____ from school for refusing to take a group shower. Also appearing in my dream is the terrifying vault horse, the very sight of which (3)_____s from my mental health. I run toward it, leap, and nose-dive into the mat.

   Next, a single (4)_____ rope threatens overhead, where it hangs from the ceiling. Wondering if anyone has ever died from rope burn, I struggle to climb it. Almost to the top, I sweat so much that I slide back to the floor, landing at the gym teacher's feet. "What a loser," the teacher mutters.

   Because I've always been (5)_____ to square-dancing, that too appears in the nightmare. Having forgotten my sneakers, I'm forced to dance in my socks on the slippery, polished floor. During one high-speed turn, I go sliding—right into the men's locker room, where the smell causes me to pass out.

   The only pleasant part of the dream comes near the end. With amazement and (6)_____, I learn that I will graduate after all.

   But then, the principal (7)_____s the terrible truth. I haven't managed to pass gym. My graduation depends on my agreeing to take four more years of gym when I get to college. If I don't, my high school diploma will be (8)_____.

SCORES:	Sentence Check 2 _____ %		Final Check _____ %

Enter your scores above and in the vocabulary performance chart on the inside back cover of the book.

Number right: 8 = 100%   7 = 88%   6 = 75%   5 = 63%   4 = 50%   3 = 38%   2 = 25%   1 = 13%

Previewing the Words

Find out how many of the eight words in this chapter you already know. Try to complete each sentence with the most suitable word from the list below. Use each word once.

Leave a sentence blank rather than guessing at an answer. Your purpose here is just to get a sense of the eight words and what you may know about them.

complacent	consensus	deplete	diligent
empathy	niche	transcend	waive

1. The fox terrier was so _____ in his digging that he soon escaped under the fence.

2. Many people believe that Shakespeare's works continue to _____ those of all other authors.

3. According to the survey, the community _____ is that a swimming pool is needed more than a new parking lot.

4. Dom spent the years after college moving restlessly from job to job, never finding a comfortable

   _____ for himself.

5. I'd like to help you out with a loan, but some unexpected car repairs have managed to

   _____ my bank account.

6. Because adults were once kids, they often have _____ for children. Kids, on the other hand, rarely identify with adults.

7. The old man decided to _____ any claim he had to the family fortune, preferring to see the money go to the younger generation.

8. The restaurant got off to a good start, but then the owners became _____ about their success and stopped trying to attract new customers.

Now check your answers by turning to page 118. Fix any mistakes and fill in any blank spaces by writing in the correct answers. By doing so, you will complete this introduction to the eight words.

You're now ready to strengthen your knowledge of the words you already know and to master the words you're only half sure of, or don't know at all. Turn to the next page.

Eight Words in Context

Figure out the meanings of the following eight words by looking *closely and carefully* at the context in which the words appear. Doing so will prepare you for the matching test and practices on the two pages that follow.

1 **complacent**
(kəm-plā'-sənt)
-adjective

   a. Elected officials cannot afford to be overly **complacent** about winning an election. Before long, they'll have to campaign again for the voters' support.

   b. Getting all A's hasn't made Ivy **complacent**. She continues to work hard at school.

2 **consensus**
(kən-sen'-səs)
-noun

   a. A vote revealed strong agreement among the teachers. The **consensus** was that they would strike if the school board did not act quickly to raise their pay.

   b. A vote revealed the family **consensus** was that we should go camping again this summer. Ray was the only one who wanted to do something else for a change.

3 **deplete**
(di-plēt')
-verb

   a. No one **depletes** my supply of sympathy faster than my brother. He's always asking for pity.

   b. In order not to **deplete** their small quantity of canned food, the survivors of the shipwreck searched the island for plants they could eat.

4 **diligent**
(dil'-ə-jənt)
-adjective

   a. I wish I had been more **diligent** about practicing piano when I was younger. It would be nice to be able to play well now.

   b. Diane was lazy when she first joined the family business, but now she's become so **diligent** that she inspires others to work harder.

5 **empathy**
(em'-pə-thē)
-noun

   a. Families who have lost loved ones in the Vietnam War have **empathy** for one another because of their shared grief.

   b. Ms. Allan is an excellent career counselor partly because of her great **empathy**. She understands each student's feelings and point of view.

6 **niche**
(nich)
-noun

   a. Although her degree was in accounting, Laura decided her **niche** was really in business management, so she went back to school for more training.

   b. Chet felt his sister's household provided a good **niche** for him since he was a bachelor who enjoyed having people of all ages around.

7 **transcend**
(tran-send')
-verb

   a. The psychic convinced her clients that she could **transcend** the restrictions of time and space and talk directly with the dead.

   b. Yoga exercises are supposed to help one **transcend** the cares of the world and reach a state of relaxation.

8 **waive**
(wāv)
-verb

   a. The defendant decided to **waive** his right to an attorney and, instead, speak for himself in court.

   b. Since Lin had studied so much math on her own, the school **waived** the requirement that she take high school algebra.

Matching Words and Definitions

Check your understanding of the eight words by matching each word with its definition. Look back at the sentences in "Eight Words in Context" as needed to decide on the meaning of each word.

_____ 1. **complacent**

_____ 2. **consensus**

_____ 3. **deplete**

_____ 4. **diligent**

_____ 5. **empathy**

_____ 6. **niche**

_____ 7. **transcend**

_____ 8. **waive**

a. the ability to share in someone else's feelings or thoughts

b. to rise above or go beyond the limits of; exceed

c. to willingly give up (as a claim, privilege, or right); do without; forgo

d. an opinion held by most or all involved

e. self-satisfied; feeling too much satisfaction with oneself or one's accomplishments

f. steady, determined, and careful in work

g. an activity or place especially suited to a person

h. to use up

CAUTION: Do not go any further until you are sure the above answers are correct. If you have studied the "Eight Words in Context," you will know how to match each word. Then you can use the matches to help you in the following practices. Your goal is to reach a point where you don't need to check definitions at all.

➤ Sentence Check 1

Complete each sentence below with the most suitable word from the box. Use each word once.

complacent	consensus	deplete	diligent
empathy	niche	transcend	waive

1. Amber offered to _____ her turn on the swing so the younger kids could use it.

2. The old man is weak, so it doesn't take much effort for him to _____ the little energy he has.

3. Fans of gymnastics believe it is an art form that _____s the ordinary world of sports.

4. If society becomes _____ about its situation, it will never move toward solving its problems.

5. Several sessions with a career counselor helped Suzanne consider what her _____ in the working world might be.

6. Arnie has been _____ in his German studies because he hopes to speak the language with his relatives from Germany when they visit next summer.

7. I had hoped the restaurant would be good, but our group's _____ was that the food was only so-so and the service was even worse.

8. Dr. Grange is a brilliant mathematician, but she has little _____ for her students. She doesn't understand how they can find some problems so difficult.

Now check your answers to these questions by turning to page 118. Going over the answers carefully will help you prepare for the next two checks, for which answers are not given.

➤ Sentence Check 2

Complete each sentence below with two words from the following list. Use each word once.

complacent	consensus	deplete	diligent
empathy	niche	transcend	waive

1-2. Lynn begged the bank to _____ the overdraft charge, telling them that the twenty

dollars would entirely _____ her savings.

3-4. In high school, Victor was voted "Most Likely to Become a Psychologist." It was the

_____ of his classmates that he was the student with the most _____

for other people.

5-6. My mother could have stayed in her comfortable _____ as part of the secretarial pool,

but she wanted to _____ the limits of that job and become an executive herself.

7-8. Dr. Roberts and Dr. Krill practice medicine very differently. Roberts is _____ about

reading journals and learning new techniques, while Krill, more _____, never tries

anything new.

➤ Final Check: A Model Teacher

Here is a final opportunity for you to strengthen your knowledge of the eight words. First read the following passage carefully. Then fill in each blank with a word from the box at the top of this page. (Context clues will help you figure out which word goes in which blank.) Use each word once.

At Eastman High School reunions, the conversation usually gets around to the question: "Which teacher do you remember best?" And year after year, the (1)_____ of the graduates is Mr. MacDonald. Many remember Joe MacDonald as the teacher against whom they measured all others.

He had started his professional life as a highly paid attorney, but never at home with that work, he left the law and found his (2) _____ as an English teacher in the shabby classrooms at Eastman. Mr. MacDonald somehow helped his students (3)_____ their broken-down surroundings until they, too, could experience the magic in the words of Shakespeare, Dickinson, or Frost. Even those who tended to avoid reading began to think there might be something to this literature stuff after all.

Mr. MacDonald never (4)_____(e)d his enthusiasm for teaching or for students. Other teachers became (5)_____ about their work and didn't put very much time into lesson preparation. But Mr. MacDonald was as (6)_____ as an eager first-year teacher. He could often be found talking with students after school, as his great (7)_____ had given him the reputation of being someone who understood students' problems. He was fun, too. On the first really beautiful spring day of each year, he'd (8)_____ his lesson plan and take the class out into the sunshine to sit under the blue sky and talk about literature.

After Mr. MacDonald's retirement, his former students wanted to honor him. They finally decided on the perfect "thank you": a college scholarship for an Eastman student, which was established in his name.

SCORES: Sentence Check 2 _____ %   **Final Check** _____ %
Enter your scores above and in the vocabulary performance chart on the inside back cover of the book.

Number right: 8 = 100%   7 = 88%   6 = 75%   5 = 63%   4 = 50%   3 = 38%   2 = 25%   1 = 13%

UNIT THREE: Test 1

PART A
Choose the word that best completes each sentence and write it in the space provided.

1. **ominous**
   complacent
   agnostic
   traumatic

   Admiring his build in the mirror, Lee gave himself a(n)

   _____ smile.

2. **benevolent**
   congenial
   ominous
   prevalent

   My boss asked me into his office in such a(n) _____ tone

   that I thought he was about to fire me.

3. **divulge**
   abstain
   endow
   aspire

   Alcohol is involved in nearly half of all U.S. traffic deaths, so

   _____ from drinking when you need to drive.

4. **elation**
   quest
   empathy
   niche

   Keith is an excellent mental health counselor who feels genuine

   _____ for those who come to him for help.

5. **diligent**
   complacent
   contemporary
   ominous

   I'm not quick with home repairs, but I'm _____. I work

   steadily and carefully until I get the job done.

6. **deficit**
   expulsion
   elation
   niche

   The _____ of Scott's parents was as great as his own joy

   and pride at winning the gymnastics competition.

7. **Quests**
   Agnostics
   Proponents
   Extroverts

   _____ of gun control point out that gun accidents in

   American homes result in over a thousand deaths each year.

8. **charisma**
   rapport
   elation
   impasse

   The talks between the two countries reached a(n) _____

   when each side claimed the oil-rich border area as its own.

9. **Flippant**
   Lucrative
   Prone
   Mandatory

   _____ to oversleeping, Sherman keeps his alarm clock

   across the room so he has to get out of bed to turn it off.

10. **charisma**
    perception
    dissent
    deficit

    If you're never able to pay off your credit-card bills, why not avoid the

    permanent _____ by tearing up the cards and paying with cash?

(Continues on next page)

PART B
Circle **C** if the italicized word is used **correctly**. Circle **I** if the word is used **incorrectly**.

C   I   11.   When I was a child, I hated broccoli, but now I'm quite *averse* to it.

C   I   12.   The *benevolent* boss laid workers off without even giving them a week's pay.

C   I   13.   That bow tie *detracts* from Alan's appearance by making him look strangled and gift-wrapped.

C   I   14.   Priests, rabbis, and other *agnostics* signed the petition asking for aid to the homeless.

C   I   15.   Eric has often had cats, but never dogs. *Conversely,* Joan has often had dogs, but never cats.

C   I   16.   A course in American history isn't *mandatory* at most colleges, but our school does require first-year students to take one.

C   I   17.   The company president was so impressed with Greta's sales record that he honored her with an *expulsion*.

C   I   18.   My sister didn't find her *niche* until she took a computer course and discovered her great talent for programming.

C   I   19.   At the restaurant, Kevin *prompted* me to save room for dessert by saying, "They make the world's best chocolate layer cake here."

C   I   20.   Halloween has *contemporary* roots. Annually, the ancient Irish would dress as demons and witches to frighten away ghosts who might otherwise claim their bodies.

SCORE: (Number correct) _____ x 5 = _____ %

Enter your scores above and in the vocabulary performance chart on the inside back cover of the book.

UNIT THREE: Test 2

PART A
Complete each sentence with a word from the box. Use each word once.

consensus	deplete	divulge	extrovert	flippant
lucrative	prevalent	quest	rapport	rationale

1. I think it's selfish of Dolly not to _____ to anyone in the family the secret recipe for her wonderful salad dressing.

2. I have an excellent _____ with my brother, but I haven't spoken to my sister for years.

3. Rudy is such a(n) _____ that he becomes friends with almost all of the customers at his beauty salon.

4. Some expensive household emergencies, such as a broken water heater, have managed to

   _____ my bank account.

5. My _____ for using cloth napkins is that they result in fewer trees being cut down for paper napkins.

6. With violent crime so _____ today, some newspaper reporters now wear bulletproof vests when they cover a story.

7. Halloween is _____ for candy manufacturers. The holiday brings in about a billion dollars a year for them.

8. The _____ among the city's sports writers is that Bridgewater High will win the basketball championship this year.

9. In some fairy tales, the hero searches far and wide, on a(n) _____ for some precious object or missing person.

10. When the principal asked Randy why he had spilled milk on some girls in the lunchroom, his

    _____ response was: "Because they were thirsty."

(Continues on next page)

PART B
Circle **C** if the italicized word is used **correctly.** Circle **I** if the word is used **incorrectly.**

C   I   11.   Sharon is *endowed* with the gift of photographic memory.

C   I   12.   Black South Africans continue their struggle to *waive* equal rights.

C   I   13.   The TV contract would be *nullified* if the star missed any more rehearsals.

C   I   14.   Whenever it snowed, the *congenial* boy next door would throw tightly packed snowballs at me.

C   I   15.   Bob's near-fatal accident was so *traumatic* for him that, a year later, he still refuses to get inside a car.

C   I   16.   When its ratings fell, the detective show was *aspired* to a new time slot on a different evening.

C   I   17.   The candidate lost the TV debate partly because of his *charisma,* which included sweating and stammering.

C   I   18.   Wayne has *transcended* his usual good grades by failing three out of his four classes this semester.

C   I   19.   The student meeting went smoothly. There was full *dissent* to give the retiring art teacher a set of fine oil paints.

C   I   20.   Fashion designers influence our *perceptions* of what is attractive. For example, who would have thought a few years ago that jeans filled with holes would be considered good looking?

> **SCORE:** (Number correct) _____ x 5 = _____ %

Enter your scores above and in the vocabulary performance chart on the inside back cover of the book.

UNIT THREE: *Test 3*

In the space provided, write the letter of the choice that is most nearly the **same** in meaning as the boldfaced word.

_____ 1. **traumatic**   a) noisy   b) dramatic   c) advanced   d) emotionally painful

_____ 2. **charisma**   a) generosity   b) health   c) charm   d) knowledge

_____ 3. **transcend**   a) cancel   b) exceed   c) happen   d) respond

_____ 4. **aspire**   a) join   b) follow   c) succeed   d) desire

_____ 5. **prone**   a) tending   b) menacing   c) talented   d) legally allowed

_____ 6. **quest**   a) sympathy   b) hope   c) proper place   d) search

_____ 7. **lucrative**   a) agreeable   b) profitable   c) common   d) expensive

_____ 8. **diligent**   a) self-satisfied   b) hardworking   c) modern   d) unlikely

_____ 9. **rapport**   a) relationship   b) explanation   c) search   d) logical basis

_____ 10. **impasse**   a) disadvantage   b) lack   c) dead end   d) meantime

_____ 11. **abstain**   a) join   b) use up   c) do without   d) long for

_____ 12. **divulge**   a) tell   b) exaggerate   c) go beyond   d) disagree

_____ 13. **niche**   a) comfort   b) assignment   c) search   d) suitable place

_____ 14. **empathy**   a) sympathy   b) great pride   c) anger   d) amusement

_____ 15. **ominous**   a) angry   b) criminal   c) threatening   d) not religious

_____ 16. **endow**   a) rise above   b) provide   c) lessen   d) have

_____ 17. **prompt**   a) discourage   b) conceal   c) agree   d) move to action

_____ 18. **rationale**   a) reasons   b) disagreement   c) great joy   d) limits

_____ 19. **nullify**   a) cancel   b) avoid   c) reveal   d) oppose

_____ 20. **perception**   a) desire   b) impression   c) knowledge   d) perfection

(Continues on next page)

PART B: Antonyms
In the space provided, write the letter of the choice that is most nearly the **opposite** in meaning to the boldfaced word.

_____ 21. **elation**   a) illness   b) sadness   c) cruelty   d) escape

_____ 22. **deficit**   a) excess   b) correctness   c) support   d) work

_____ 23. **contemporary**   a) popular   b) antique   c) uncommon   d) unimproved

_____ 24. **deplete**   a) prefer   b) occur   c) lose   d) increase

_____ 25. **agnostic**   a) doubter of God   b) loner   c) believer in God   d) prophet

_____ 26. **benevolent**   a) cruel   b) unhappy   c) poor   d) conceited

_____ 27. **extrovert**   a) opponent   b) worker   c) leader   d) loner

_____ 28. **averse**   a) effective   b) tending toward   c) doubting   d) done slowly

_____ 29. **dissent**   a) agreement   b) pleasure   c) success   d) prediction

_____ 30. **consensus**   a) full count   b) majority   c) impression   d) minority opinion

_____ 31. **detract**   a) conclude   b) remember   c) add to   d) face

_____ 32. **expulsion**   a) recognition   b) welcoming   c) payment   d) regret

_____ 33. **congenial**   a) in doubt   b) far away   c) dissatisfied   d) disagreeable

_____ 34. **prevalent**   a) incorrect   b) difficult   c) uncommon   d) unpopular

_____ 35. **waive**   a) claim   b) forgive   c) go below   d) oppose

_____ 36. **mandatory**   a) unnecessary   b) easy   c) welcome   d) unlikely

_____ 37. **complacent**   a) different   b) self-doubting   c) uncomplicated   d) trustworthy

_____ 38. **proponent**   a) newcomer   b) inner-directed person   c) opponent   d) voter

_____ 39. **conversely**   a) expertly   b) boldly   c) late   d) in the same way

_____ 40. **flippant**   a) silent   b) persistent   c) curious   d) respectful

SCORE: (Number correct) _____ x 2.5 = _____ %

Enter your scores above and in the vocabulary performance chart on the inside back cover of the book.

UNIT THREE: Test 4

PART A

Complete each sentence in a way that clearly shows you understand the meaning of the boldfaced word. Take a minute to plan your answer before you write.

Example: I **abstain** from _____ *smoking. I don't want to get lung cancer.* _____

1. Luis showed his **elation** at the news by _____

   _____

2. I **aspire** to _____

   _____

3. Jane, who is a **proponent** of daily exercise, advised me, " _____

   _____

4. At our school, it is **mandatory** that students _____

   _____

5. At parties, my **extrovert** friend _____

   _____

6. I find it **detracts** from a restaurant meal when _____

   _____

7. Lamont is **averse** to city life because _____

   _____

8. Our father told us how **traumatic** it was for him to _____

   _____

9. My **rationale** for going to college is _____

   _____

10. When asked by the restaurant owner to pay his bill, the young man's **flippant** reply was: " _____

   _____

(Continues on next page)

PART B

After each boldfaced word are a *synonym* (a word that means the same as the boldfaced word), an *antonym* (a word that means the opposite of the boldfaced word), and a word that is neither. Mark the synonym with an *S* and the antonym with an *A*.

Example: **prevalent**	_____ heavy	_A_ rare	_S_ common
11-12. **contemporary**	_____ modern	_____ rapid	_____ ancient
13-14. **divulge**	_____ reveal	_____ conceal	_____ defend
15-16. **benevolent**	_____ evil	_____ gifted	_____ kind
17-18. **congenial**	_____ clever	_____ pleasant	_____ disagreeable
19-20. **diligent**	_____ lazy	_____ believable	_____ hardworking

PART C

Use five of the following ten words in sentences. Make it clear that you know the meaning of the word you use. Feel free to use the past tense or plural form of a word.

consensus	deplete	dissent	empathy	niche
perception	prone	quest	rapport	waive

21. _____

_____

22. _____

_____

23. _____

_____

24. _____

_____

25. _____

SCORE: (Number correct) _____ x 4 = _____ %

Enter your scores above and in the vocabulary performance chart on the inside back cover of the book.

Previewing the Words

Find out how many of the eight words in this chapter you already know. Try to complete each sentence with the most suitable word from the list below. Use each word once.

Leave a sentence blank rather than guessing at an answer. Your purpose here is just to get a sense of the eight words and what you may know about them.

condone	contemplate	feign	furtive
gape	pathetic	precedent	punitive

1. Two young children stepped closer to _____ at the clown, but when he approached them, they hid their faces.

2. Shy Dennis stole a _____ glance at the woman he liked, but he was afraid to approach her.

3. Our father had a _____ nature. He tended to spank us for every wrongdoing, however small.

4. I _____(e)d vacationing in Hawaii, but I decided that my budget wouldn't allow such an expensive trip.

5. Crystal will often _____ illness to avoid work. She may fool her supervisor, but she doesn't fool me.

6. I don't _____ Barb's habit of smoking in public because it annoys other people and threatens their health.

7. My sit-ups are _____. They're so weak that they look like neck-ups.

8. "I'd like to give you a day off to go to the World Series," said Calvin's boss. "But I'd be setting a

    _____ that other employees would use to go to events they'd want to see."

Now check your answers by turning to page 119. Fix any mistakes and fill in any blank spaces by writing in the correct answers. By doing so, you will complete this introduction to the eight words.

You're now ready to strengthen your knowledge of the words you already know and to master the words you're only half sure of, or don't know at all. Turn to the next page.

Eight Words in Context

Figure out the meanings of the following eight words by looking *closely and carefully* at the context in which the words appear. Doing so will prepare you for the matching test and practices on the two pages that follow.

1 **condone**
(kən-dōn')
-verb

    a. "I can't stop you," Ms. Mather told her daughter, "but neither can I **condone** your plan to live with Allen without being married to him."

    b. I can overlook it when you're five minutes late. But how can I **condone** your walking in to work an hour late?

2 **contemplate**
(kon'-təm-plāt')
-verb

    a. Because Ben hadn't studied for the test, he **contemplated** cheating. He quickly realized, however, that the eagle-eyed teacher would spot him.

    b. Whenever Anne's husband drank too much, she would **contemplate** divorce, but then she would feel guilty for thinking about leaving a sick man.

3 **feign**
(fān)
-verb

    a. My bosses only **feigned** concern about my financial difficulties. They really didn't care.

    b. You can **feign** a head cold by pretending you're too stuffed up to pronounce an *l*, *n*, or *m*. Try it by saying, "I have a code id by dose."

4 **furtive**
(fûr'-tiv)
-adjective

    a. I wondered why Cathy's behavior was so **furtive** until I discovered twenty people gathered for a surprise party in my honor.

    b. According to experts, teenagers who are **furtive** about where they are going and with whom may be involved with drugs.

5 **gape**
(gāp)
-verb

    a. Everyone stopped to **gape** at the odd-looking sculpture in front of the library.

    b. Because drivers slowed down to **gape** at an accident in the southbound lanes, northbound traffic was backed up for miles.

6 **pathetic**
(pə-thet'-ik)
-adjective

    a. That plumber's work was **pathetic**. Not only does the faucet still drip, but now the pipe is leaking.

    b. Health care in some areas of the world is **pathetic**. People are dying of diseases that are easily treatable with modern medicine.

7 **precedent**
(pres'-i-dənt)
-noun

    a. When Jean's employer gave her three months off after her baby was born, a **precedent** was set for any other woman in the firm who became pregnant.

    b. To set a **precedent**, the teacher gave the student who stole an exam an F for the entire course. "Others will think twice before they do the same," he explained.

8 **punitive**
(pyōō'-ni-tiv)
-adjective

    a. Judge Stam is especially **punitive** with drunk drivers, giving every one of them a jail term.

    b. Many parents find that reward is a better basis for teaching children than **punitive** action is.

Matching Words and Definitions

Check your understanding of the eight words by matching each word with its definition. Look back at the sentences in "Eight Words in Context" as needed to decide on the meaning of each word.

_____ 1. **condone**	a. done or behaving in a secretive way
_____ 2. **contemplate**	b. to stare in wonder or amazement
_____ 3. **feign**	c. anything that may serve as an example in dealing with later similar circumstances
_____ 4. **furtive**	d. to forgive or overlook
_____ 5. **gape**	e. giving or involving punishment; punishing
_____ 6. **pathetic**	f. to think about seriously
_____ 7. **precedent**	g. pitifully lacking or unsuccessful; so inadequate as to be ridiculous
_____ 8. **punitive**	h. to pretend; give a false show of

CAUTION: Do not go any further until you are sure the above answers are correct. If you have studied the "Eight Words in Context," you will know how to match each word. Then you can use the matches to help you in the following practices. Your goal is to reach a point where you don't need to check definitions at all.

➤ Sentence Check 1

Complete each sentence below with the most suitable word from the box. Use each word once.

condone	contemplate	feign	furtive
gape	pathetic	precedent	punitive

1. Handicapped people don't like others to _____ at them. Instead of a stare, a simple smile would be appreciated.

2. From time to time, I _____ attending business school, but so far I've made no firm decision.

3. Lawyers can strengthen a case by finding a useful _____ among previous similar cases.

4. The principal does not _____ hitting students. He believes every problem has a nonviolent solution.

5. The people on the elevator didn't want to stare at the patch on my eye, but several took

   _____ glances.

6. Old Mr. Hall's living conditions were _____. There was no heat or electricity in his apartment, and the walls were crumbling.

7. When I had to give an oral report in class, I tried to _____ confidence, but my shaking legs revealed my nervousness.

8. My mother wasn't usually _____, but one day I pushed her too far, and she said, "If you do that one more time, I will send you to your room for the rest of your adolescence."

Now check your answers to these questions by turning to page 119. Going over the answers carefully will help you prepare for the next two checks, for which answers are not given.

➤ Sentence Check 2

Complete each sentence below with two words from the box. Use each word once.

condone	contemplate	feign	furtive
gape	pathetic	precedent	punitive

1-2. Some parents take only _____ measures when children misbehave. They never take

time to _____ the benefits of a gentler approach.

3-4. Several commuters stopped to _____ at the homeless man and his

_____ shelter, made of cardboard and a torn blanket.

5-6. The fourth-grade teacher said, "I will not _____ any _____

behavior in my class. Rita, please read out loud the note you secretly passed to Ellen."

7-8. The _____ was set many years ago: When the winner of a beauty contest is

announced, the runner-up _____s happiness for the winner, no matter how she
actually feels.

➤ Final Check: Shoplifter

Here is a final opportunity for you to strengthen your knowledge of the eight words. First read the following passage carefully. Then fill in each blank with a word from the box at the top of this page. (Context clues will help you figure out which word goes in which blank.) Use each word once.

Valerie took a (1)_____ glance around her. When it seemed no one was watching, she

stuffed a blue shirt into her purse and darted out of the store. "Stop! You! Stop!" shouted a guard who

seemed to appear from nowhere. Then another man in street clothes grabbed her purse and pulled out the

shirt.

"But. . . but . . . It's not mine. I don't know how it got there," Valerie cried.

The two men just looked at each other and laughed. The guard said, "That's what they all say. People

steal without taking time to (2)_____ the possible results. Then when they're caught, they

(3)_____ innocence."

As the guard began to phone the police, Valerie begged, "Please don't press charges. Please. This is the

first time I've ever done anything like this, and I'll never do it again."

The men laughed again. "Your argument is (4)_____," the man in street clothes said.

"It's everyone's first time. Our store always presses charges against shoplifting. We can't set the bad

(5)_____ of letting a shoplifter go, as if we (6)_____(e)d such crimes."

"That's right," said the guard. "This shirt only costs twenty dollars, but the twenties add up. We lost

about $150,000 worth of merchandise to shoplifters last year. We have no choice but to take

(7)_____ action."

Soon Valerie was led to the police car. She covered her face as other shoppers stopped to

(8)_____ at the lovely young woman, an unlikely-looking criminal.

SCORES: Sentence Check 2 _____ %   Final Check _____ %

Enter your scores above and in the vocabulary performance chart on the inside back cover of the book.

Number right: 8 = 100%   7 = 88%   6 = 75%   5 = 63%   4 = 50%   3 = 38%   2 = 25%   1 = 13%

Previewing the Words

Find out how many of the eight words in this chapter you already know. Try to complete each sentence with the most suitable word from the list below. Use each word once.

Leave a sentence blank rather than guessing at an answer. Your purpose here is just to get a sense of the eight words and what you may know about them.

deficient	detrimental	implicit	inhibition
ironic	rupture	saturate	vindictive

1. My cat and I have a(n) _____ understanding that when I open a can of sardines, she gets some too.

2. It's not necessary to _____ your paint brush. Just pick up enough paint to coat the tip.

3. It's _____ that Loretta is such a strict mother because she was certainly wild in her youth.

4. My brother's _____(s) about women are the result of an unhappy romance he had several years ago.

5. Even something as healthy-sounding as vitamins can be _____ to your health when taken in large quantities.

6. Gil is _____ in good manners. For example, I've never heard him thank anyone for anything.

7. The bulge in the baby's stomach was caused by a muscle wall that _____(e)d and would have to be repaired.

8. When he was denied permission to have another cookie, the _____ child aimed a kick right at his aunt's weak ankle.

Now check your answers by turning to page 119. Fix any mistakes and fill in any blank spaces by writing in the correct answers. By doing so, you will complete this introduction to the eight words.

You're now ready to strengthen your knowledge of the words you already know and to master the words you're only half sure of, or don't know at all. Turn to the next page.

Eight Words in Context

Figure out the meanings of the following eight words by looking *closely and carefully* at the context in which the words appear. Doing so will prepare you for the matching test and practices on the two pages that follow.

1 **deficient**
(di-fish'-ənt)
-adjective

    a. When people have too little iron in their blood, it sometimes means that their diet is also **deficient** in iron.

    b. The living room is **deficient** in light. We need to get another lamp.

2 **detrimental**
(de'-trə-men'-təl)
-adjective

    a. Do you think all television is **detrimental** to a child, or are some programs good for kids?

    b. The gases from automobiles and factories have been so **detrimental** to the environment that some of the damage may be permanent.

3 **implicit**
(im-plis'-it)
-adjective

    a. When the gangster growled, "I'm sure you want your family to stay well," Harris understood the **implicit** threat.

    b. Although it's never been said, there's an **implicit** understanding that Carla will be promoted when Earl finally retires.

4 **inhibition**
(in'-hə-bish'-ən)
-noun

    a. A two-year-old has no **inhibition** about running around naked.

    b. Sarah's family is openly affectionate, with no **inhibitions** toward hugging or kissing in public.

5 **ironic**
(ī-ron'-ik)
-adjective

    a. "Ken better get his act together" was Beth's **ironic** comment when she heard he had gotten straight A's that semester.

    b. "The Gift of the Magi" is a short story with an **ironic** twist: A woman sells her long hair to buy a chain for her husband's watch, while her husband sells his watch to buy combs for her hair.

6 **rupture**
(rup'-chər)
-verb

    a. If the dam were to **rupture**, the town would disappear under many feet of water.

    b. Victims of the Black Death, the fatal disease that swept Europe in the mid-1300's, often developed swellings that **ruptured** near the time of death.

7 **saturate**
(sach'-ə-rāt')
-verb

    a. Most people like their cereal crunchy, but Teresa lets hers sit until the milk has **saturated** every piece.

    b. After studying history for three hours, my brain was so **saturated** that I couldn't have absorbed one more bit of information.

8 **vindictive**
(vin-dik'-tiv)
-adjective

    a. If a woman refuses to date Leon, he becomes **vindictive**. One way he takes revenge is to insult the woman in public.

    b. After she was given two weeks' notice, the **vindictive** employee intentionally jumbled the company's files.

Matching Words and Definitions

Check your understanding of the eight words by matching each word with its definition. Look back at the sentences in "Eight Words in Context" as needed to decide on the meaning of each word.

_____ 1. **deficient**   a. a holding back or block of some action, feeling, or thought

_____ 2. **detrimental**   b. suggested but not directly expressed; unstated, but able to be understood

_____ 3. **implicit**   c. vengeful; inclined to seek revenge

_____ 4. **inhibition**   d. to burst or break apart

_____ 5. **ironic**   e. lacking some characteristic or element

_____ 6. **rupture**   f. to soak, load, or fill as much as possible

_____ 7. **saturate**   g. harmful

_____ 8. **vindictive**   h. meaning the opposite of what is said; being opposite to what might be expected

CAUTION: Do not go any further until you are sure the above answers are correct. If you have studied the "Eight Words in Context," you will know how to match each word. Then you can use the matches to help you in the following practices. Your goal is to reach a point where you don't need to check definitions at all.

➤ Sentence Check 1

Complete each sentence below with the most suitable word from the box. Use each word once.

deficient	detrimental	implicit	inhibition
ironic	rupture	saturate	vindictive

1. A person can be intelligent and yet be _____ in common sense.

2. When the pressure in the gas pipe became too great, the pipe _____(e)d.

3. Isn't it _____ that the richest man in town should win the million dollar lottery?

4. That ugly factory building is certainly _____ to the neighborhood's appearance.

5. Becky's customary lack of _____ was evident the time she came to class barefoot.

6. Street gangs are _____. If anyone harms a member of a gang, the other members will take full revenge.

7. The aroma of Gretchen's perfume so _____(e)d the air in the car that Steve coughed and rolled down a window.

8. While it's not written in teachers' contracts, there is a(n) _____ understanding that teachers will spend time preparing lessons and responding to students' work.

Now check your answers to these questions by turning to page 119. Going over the answers carefully will help you prepare for the next two checks, for which answers are not given.

➤ Sentence Check 2

Complete each sentence below with two words from the box. Use each word once.

deficient	detrimental	implicit	inhibition
ironic	rupture	saturate	vindictive

1-2. Water balloon fights are fun until a balloon _____s against your clothes, and they get _____(e)d with cold water.

3-4. My sister is always trying to "get even" with someone. Her _____ attitude is _____ to her relationships with family and friends.

5-6. It's _____ that the book *Live Simply on Little Money* has made the author wealthy since a(n) _____ message of the book is that the author himself requires little money.

7-8. Gerry feels people should "lose their _____s" and do whatever they feel like doing, but I think people who are altogether _____ in self-control have poor manners.

➤ Final Check: A Nutty Newspaper Office

Here is a final opportunity for you to strengthen your knowledge of the eight words. First read the following passage carefully. Then fill in each blank with a word from the box at the top of this page. (Context clues will help you figure out which word goes in which blank.) Use each word once.

· My therapist says it's (1)_____ to my mental health to keep my thoughts bottled up inside of me, so I'll drop all (2)_____s and tell you about the newspaper office where I work.

Let me describe my editor first. It's sort of (3)_____ that Ed is in communications because I've never met anyone harder to talk to. I'll say, "How are you doing today, Ed?" and he'll say something like "The tidal pools of time are catching up with me." I used to think there might be some deep wisdom (4)_____ in Ed's statements, but now I just think he's a little crazy.

Then there's Seymour, our sports writer. Seymour is perfectly normal except that he has unexplained fits of crying two or three times a week. You'll be in the middle of a conversation about the Mets or something and suddenly Seymour has started to (5)_____ handfuls of Kleenex with his tears.

Don't think our office is boring or depressing, though. It is not entirely (6)_____ in excitement, but even our excitement is a little weird. It is usually provided by Jan, a (7)_____ typesetter who, whenever irritated by Ed, takes revenge in some horrible but entertaining way. One of her favorite ways is sneaking fictional items about him into the society column. I'll never forget the time Ed was in the hospital after his appendix (8)_____(e)d. He almost broke his stitches when he read that he was taking a vacation at a nudist colony.

SCORES: Sentence Check 2 _____%   Final Check _____%
Enter your scores above and in the vocabulary performance chart on the inside back cover of the book.

Number right: 8 = 100%   7 = 88%   6 = 75%   5 = 63%   4 = 50%   3 = 38%   2 = 25%   1 = 13%

Previewing the Words

Find out how many of the eight words in this chapter you already know. Try to complete each sentence with the most suitable word from the list below. Use each word once.

Leave a sentence blank rather than guessing at an answer. Your purpose here is just to get a sense of the eight words and what you may know about them.

constrict	exhaustive	fallible	formulate
habitat	pragmatic	reconcile	vile

1. If my daughter's jeans were any tighter, they would _____ the blood flowing to her feet.

2. If you intend to open a restaurant, you must first _____ a careful business plan.

3. Everyone is _____, but there's no need to make the same mistakes over and over again.

4. "Hang your food bag from a pole at night," the park ranger warned. "This area is a bear

_____."

5. After the motorcycle accident, Sheena had to _____ herself to the limited use of her right hand.

6. My sister loves a certain cheese that has the _____ odor of something that fell off a garbage truck.

7. The Chinese restaurant's menu was the most _____ I'd ever seen. It listed many dishes I'd never even heard of.

8. Lloyd is so concerned about looking good that sometimes he isn't at all _____. Once he wore a suit and a silk tie to a company softball game.

Now check your answers by turning to page 119. Fix any mistakes and fill in any blank spaces by writing in the correct answers. By doing so, you will complete this introduction to the eight words.

You're now ready to strengthen your knowledge of the words you already know and to master the words you're only half sure of, or don't know at all. Turn to the next page.

Eight Words in Context

Figure out the meanings of the following eight words by looking *closely and carefully* at the context in which the words appear. Doing so will prepare you for the matching test and practices on the two pages that follow.

1 **constrict**
(kən-strikt')
-verb

    a. The summer highway construction will **constrict** traffic to the width of only two lanes.

    b. For centuries in China, girls' feet were **constricted** with binding to keep them from growing to normal size. Women's feet were considered most attractive if they were under four inches long.

2 **exhaustive**
(eg-zôs'-tiv)
-adjective

    a. Don't buy a used car without putting it through an **exhaustive** inspection. Check every detail, from hood to trunk.

    b. My teacher recommended an **exhaustive** thousand-page biography of Freud, but who has time to read such a thorough account?

3 **fallible**
(fal'-ə-bəl)
-adjective

    a. "I know everyone is **fallible**," the boss told his workers. "But do you have to make so many of your mistakes on company time?"

    b. When they are little, kids think their parents can do no wrong, but when they become teenagers, their parents suddenly become quite **fallible**.

4 **formulate**
(for'-myōo-lāt')
-verb

    a. Before stepping into his boss's office, Hank had carefully **formulated** his case for a raise.

    b. The author first **formulated** an outline of his plot and then began writing his mystery.

5 **habitat**
(hab'-i-tat)
-noun

    a. A growing number of people believe that wild animals should be allowed to remain in their natural **habitats** and not be captured and put in zoos.

    b. Although we think of the forest as the **habitat** of raccoons, many raccoons live in cities where food is plentiful.

6 **pragmatic**
(prag-mat'-ik)
-adjective

    a. We always called my sister "Practical Polly" because she was the most **pragmatic** member of the family.

    b. When I was young and single, I spent most of my money on travel. Now that I have a family to support, I must spend my money in more **pragmatic** ways.

7 **reconcile**
(rek'-ən-sīl')
-verb

    a. When my grandfather died, we worked hard to **reconcile** Grandmother to the fact that he was really gone.

    b. After his third wreck in six months, Tony **reconciled** himself to living somewhere along a bus line and doing without a car.

8 **vile**
(vīl)
-adjective

    a. Piles of wet garbage sitting in the summer sun soon acquire a **vile** smell.

    b. When I finally get around to cleaning out my refrigerator, I always find some **vile** moldy food at the back of a shelf.

Matching Words and Definitions

Check your understanding of the eight words by matching each word with its definition. Look back at the sentences in "Eight Words in Context" as needed to decide on the meaning of each word.

_____ 1. **constrict**   a. to bring (oneself or someone else) to accept

_____ 2. **exhaustive**   b. the natural environment of an animal or plant

_____ 3. **fallible**   c. capable of making an error

_____ 4. **formulate**   d. to make smaller or narrower, as by squeezing or shrinking

_____ 5. **habitat**   e. covering all possible details; complete; thorough

_____ 6. **pragmatic**   f. offensive to the senses, feelings, or thoughts; disgusting

_____ 7. **reconcile (to)**   g. to form or work out in one's mind; develop

_____ 8. **vile**   h. practical

> *CAUTION*: Do not go any further until you are sure the above answers are correct. If you have studied the "Eight Words in Context," you will know how to match each word. Then you can use the matches to help you in the following practices. Your goal is to reach a point where you don't need to check definitions at all.

➤*Sentence Check 1*

Complete each sentence below with the most suitable word from the box. Use each word once.

constrict	exhaustive	fallible	formulate
habitat	pragmatic	reconcile	vile

1. Our cafeteria serves the world's most _____ beef stew, full of big globs of fat.

2. My mother was forced to _____ herself to my independence when I moved into my own apartment.

3. Bright light _____s the pupils of our eyes. Darkness makes them wider, letting more light in.

4. My supervisor told me that if I wished to work on an independent project, I should

   _____ a detailed plan of my idea.

5. For her term paper on orchids, Wilma did _____ research, covering every aspect of the flower's growth and marketing.

6. Children's stories sometimes mistakenly show penguins at the North Pole. The birds'

   _____ is actually near the South Pole.

7. "It would be more _____," my daughter said, "if you went to the grocery once a week for a larger order rather than going daily for just a few items."

8. When the auto mechanic said, "Well, I'm _____ like everyone else," I responded, "Yes, but your mistake almost got me flattened by a truck."

Now check your answers to these questions by turning to page 119. Going over the answers carefully will help you prepare for the next two checks, for which answers are not given.

➤ Sentence Check 2

Complete each sentence below with two words from the box. Use each word once.

constrict	exhaustive	fallible	formulate
habitat	pragmatic	reconcile	vile

1-2. "You want me to be perfect, but that's impossible!" my daughter cried. "_____

yourself to the fact that every one of us is _____."

3-4. Wildlife experts _____(e)d a plan by which to preserve what little remains of the

gorilla's natural _____.

5-6. My roommate was not at all _____. He would spend our household money on

videotapes and _____-smelling cigars and leave us without food.

7-8. When our pet python escaped, we quickly made a(n) _____ search throughout the

house and grounds. We found him wrapped around our dog, about to _____ the poor

mutt to death.

➤ Final Check: Roughing It

Here is a final opportunity for you to strengthen your knowledge of the eight words. First read the following passage carefully. Then fill in each blank with a word from the box at the top of this page. (Context clues will help you figure out which word goes in which blank.) Use each word once.

"Whose brilliant idea was this anyway?" Sara asked. "If people were intended to sleep on the ground and cook over a fire, we wouldn't have invented beds and microwave ovens."

"Stop complaining," Emily said. "At least you've got dry clothes on. You didn't end up walking through some (1)_____ mud because your canoe overturned. And you didn't have a partner who claimed to know everything about canoeing but actually didn't know enough to steer around a rock."

"So I made a mistake," George said. "We're all (2)_____."

"Well," Emily responded, "your mistake cost us our tent. And our sleeping bags and clothes are soaked."

Doug spoke up. "It's no big deal. Sara and I will lend you clothes, and you two can squeeze into our tent."

"Squeeze is right, " said Emily. "Four in one tent will (3)_____ us so much that we won't be able to exhale."

"It's your choice," said Doug. "Would you rather sleep in a crowded tent or outside in a wild-animal (4)_____?"

Sara couldn't resist adding, "If you had listened to me and were more (5)_____ when planning for this trip, we wouldn't be in such a mess. You would have written a(n) (6)_____ list of exactly what items would be needed, from A to Z . Then you would have (7)_____(e)d a clear plan for who would take what. Then we wouldn't be out here with two corkscrews but no plastic to wrap our belongings in."

"Let's just stop complaining," said Doug. "We need to (8)_____ ourselves to the fact that we are in this mess together, and then get back to having a good time."

SCORES: Sentence Check 2 _____ %   **Final Check** _____ %

Enter your scores above and in the vocabulary performance chart on the inside back cover of the book.

Number right: 8 = 100%   7 = 88%   6 = 75%   5 = 63%   4 = 50%   3 = 38%   2 = 25%   1 = 13%

Previewing the Words

Find out how many of the eight words in this chapter you already know. Try to complete each sentence with the most suitable word from the list below. Use each word once.

Leave a sentence blank rather than guessing at an answer. Your purpose here is just to get a sense of the eight words and what you may know about them.

avid	**dwindle**	esteem	legacy
muted	**nurture**	pacify	transient

1. Julie wants a lasting relationship, but Evan seems interested in only _____ ones.

2. The day's brightness continued to _____ as more and more clouds blocked the sun.

3. The critics held the play in such high _____ that they voted it "Best Play of the Year."

4. At the party, Yoko and I kept our conversation _____ so that no one would overhear us.

5. The quickest way to _____ the angry employees was to meet their demand for higher wages.

6. Todd is a(n) _____ sportsman who spends much of his free time jogging and playing basketball.

7. Some birds feed their young with fresh insects. Others _____ their newborn with partially digested food from their own mouths.

8. Ana's great-grandfather, grandmother, and mother were all musicians. She must have inherited the

   _____ of musical talent because she's an excellent piano and guitar player.

Now check your answers by turning to page 119. Fix any mistakes and fill in any blank spaces by writing in the correct answers. By doing so, you will complete this introduction to the eight words.

You're now ready to strengthen your knowledge of the words you already know and to master the words you're only half sure of, or don't know at all. Turn to the next page.

Eight Words in Context

Figure out the meanings of the following eight words by looking *closely and carefully* at the context in which the words appear. Doing so will prepare you for the matching test and practices on the two pages that follow.

1 **avid**
(av'-id)
-adjective

a. Rich, an **avid** reader, enjoys nothing more than a good science-fiction novel.

b. My sister is such an **avid** fan of Michael Jackson that her bedroom walls are covered with posters of him and she has taken to wearing white gloves.

2 **dwindle**
(dwin'-dəl)
-verb

a. As the number of leaves on the tree **dwindled**, the number on the ground increased.

b. The nicotine gum helped Jane's craving for cigarettes to **dwindle** down to two cigarettes a day. Soon she quit altogether.

3 **esteem**
(e-stēm')
-noun

a. When Mr. Cranston retired after teaching gym and coaching for thirty years, his admiring students gave him a gold whistle as a sign of their **esteem**.

b. In some countries, people show **esteem** with a bow from the waist or other actions, but such gestures of respect are rare in the U.S.

4 **legacy**
(leg'-ə-sē)
-noun

a. In many legends, after someone commits a terrible crime, that person's entire family is cursed for all time. This **legacy** is the victim's lasting revenge.

b. One of my mother's richest **legacies** to me was her love of nature. I've inherited her interests in growing flowers and in hiking.

5 **muted**
(myōō'-təd)
-adjective

a. When I put on my earplugs, the yelling from the next apartment becomes **muted** enough so that it no longer disturbs me.

b. The artist used **muted** rather than bright colors, to give the painting a soft, peaceful tone.

6 **nurture**
(nûr'-chər)
-verb

a. While I often forget to water or feed my plants, my sister carefully **nurtures** her many ferns and violets.

b. In general, female fish do not **nurture** their young by feeding and protecting them. They only lay the eggs, which are guarded by the male until hatching.

7 **pacify**
(pas'-ə-fī')
-verb

a. When I'm feeling nervous or upset, I often **pacify** myself with a soothing cup of mint tea.

b. Not only did I anger Roberta by calling her boyfriend "a creep," but I failed to **pacify** her with my note of apology: "I'm sorry I called Mel a creep. It's not always wise to tell the truth."

8 **transient**
(tran'-shənt)
-adjective

a. The drug's dangers include both **transient** side effects, such as temporarily blurred vision, and permanent brain damage.

b. Some hotels have only **transient** guests; others welcome permanent residents as well.

Matching Words and Definitions

Check your understanding of the eight words by matching each word with its definition. Look back at the sentences in "Eight Words in Context" as needed to decide on the meaning of each word.

_____ 1. **avid**		a. softened; toned down; made less intense
_____ 2. **dwindle**		b. temporary; passing soon or quickly
_____ 3. **esteem**		c. enthusiastic and devoted
_____ 4. **legacy**		d. to make calm or peaceful
_____ 5. **muted**		e. to gradually lessen or shrink
_____ 6. **nurture**		f. a high regard; respect; favorable opinion
_____ 7. **pacify**		g. to promote the development of by providing nourishment, support, and protection
_____ 8. **transient**		h. something handed down from people who have come before

CAUTION: Do not go any further until you are sure the above answers are correct. If you have studied the "Eight Words in Context," you will know how to match each word. Then you can use the matches to help you in the following practices. Your goal is to reach a point where you don't need to check definitions at all.

➤ Sentence Check 1

Complete each sentence below with the most suitable word from the box. Use each word once.

avid	dwindle	esteem	legacy
muted	nurture	pacify	transient

1. You must _____ a child with love and respect as well as with food and shelter.

2. If you study too long at one sitting, your concentration will eventually begin to _____.

3. To me, a _____ trumpet has a much more pleasant sound than one blowing at full volume.

4. When my newborn nephew starts to scream, we _____ him by rocking him and singing softly.

5. Part of spring's charm is that it's _____. It comes and goes so quickly that I can't wait for its return.

6. To show his _____ for her singing, the talent agent sent Mary daisies after she performed in a local theatre.

7. My cousin Bobby is the most _____ collector I know. He collects almost anything, from baseball cards to beer cans.

8. Shakespeare's work, a priceless _____ from the 16th and 17th centuries, has been enjoyed by generation after generation.

Now check your answers to these questions by turning to page 119. Going over the answers carefully will help you prepare for the next two checks, for which answers are not given.

➤ Sentence Check 2

Complete each sentence below with two words from the box. Use each word once.

avid	dwindle	esteem	legacy
muted	nurture	pacify	transient

1-2. Loud music upsets our canary, but _____ tones _____ her.

3-4. Della's _____ for Rick turned out to be _____. She lost respect for him when she saw him buy drugs.

5-6. Leo is such a(n) _____ chef that his enthusiasm for cooking never _____s. He's been known to cook happily for ten straight hours.

7-8. It is necessary to _____ a human infant since it is the biological _____ of newborn mammals to be unable to survive on their own.

➤ Final Check: Getting Scared

Here is a final opportunity for you to strengthen your knowledge of the eight words. First read the following passage carefully. Then fill in each blank with a word from the box at the top of this page. (Context clues will help you figure out which word goes in which blank.) Use each word once.

Remember trying to scare yourself and everybody else when you were a kid? For instance, maybe you were a(n) (1)_____ roller-coaster rider, closing your eyes and screaming and loving it all. Afterwards, you would (2)_____ your still nervous stomach by sipping quietly away at an ice-cold Coke. If a short roller-coaster ride gave you too (3)_____ a thrill, there was always the long-term fear of a horror movie. If the movie was a good one, you might be scared about going to bed for the next three months.

And remember popping out from behind corners yelling "Boo!" at your brother? The fight that followed ("You didn't scare me one bit." "Did too." "Did not." "Did too.") would go on until a grown-up ended the conflict. (Parents always seemed to be there to settle disputes or to (4)_____ and reassure you at times when you needed support.)

At other times, you and your friends probably sat around a campfire late at night, telling ghost stories. Thrilled with the horror of it all, you spoke in voices so (5)_____ they were almost whispers. The storyteller who gained the most (6)_____ was the one who told the most frightening story. If anybody's fear started to (7)_____, this expert would build it up again with the story of the ghost of the outhouse, a (8)_____ handed down from older brothers and sisters to younger ones. The story always made you so scared that you needed to go to the outhouse. But fearing the ghost there, how could you?

SCORES: Sentence Check 2 _____ %   **Final Check** _____ %

Enter your scores above and in the vocabulary performance chart on the inside back cover of the book.

Number right: 8 = 100%   7 = 88%   6 = 75%   5 = 63%   4 = 50%   3 = 38%   2 = 25%   1 = 13%

Previewing the Words

Find out how many of the eight words in this chapter you already know. Try to complete each sentence with the most suitable word from the list below. Use each word once.

Leave a sentence blank rather than guessing at an answer. Your purpose here is just to get a sense of the eight words and what you may know about them.

aloof	ambivalent	augment	dispel
explicit	longevity	magnitude	render

1. Giant redwood trees have great _____, sometimes surviving for thousands of years.

2. When the bank teller realized the _____ of his error, he panicked at the thought of being held responsible for the loss of so large a sum of money.

3. Anita said, "I'm _____ about the dress. I like the style but not that green-yellow color."

4. Because of her _____ personality, Wendy is not as popular as Lynn, who is much less cool and reserved.

5. The choir director said, "Let's _____ the sound by adding more singers instead of increasing microphone volume."

6. The doctor's explanation was _____. He explained Bonnie's surgery to her in detail, using illustrations for even greater clarity.

7. A grade of A on the final exam would _____ any doubts Sheila may still have about her ability to succeed in computer science.

8. Staring at the sun for even a short time can _____ a person blind.

Now check your answers by turning to page 119. Fix any mistakes and fill in any blank spaces by writing in the correct answers. By doing so, you will complete this introduction to the eight words.

You're now ready to strengthen your knowledge of the words you already know and to master the words you're only half sure of, or don't know at all. Turn to the next page.

Eight Words in Context

Figure out the meanings of the following eight words by looking *closely and carefully* at the context in which the words appear. Doing so will prepare you for the matching test and practices on the two pages that follow.

1 **aloof**
(ə-lōof')
-adjective

   a. Some people say that the English are **aloof**, but the ones I've met seem warm and open.

   b. I knew that Taylor was upset with me about something because he was cool and **aloof** even when I tried to be friendly.

2 **ambivalent**
(am-biv'-ə-lənt)
-adjective

   a. "Because I'm **ambivalent** about marriage," Earl said, "I keep swinging back and forth between wanting to set the date and wanting to break off my engagement."

   b. I'm **ambivalent** about my mother-in-law. I appreciate her desire to be helpful, but I dislike her efforts to run our lives.

3 **augment**
(ôg-ment')
-verb

   a. Why do women **augment** their height with high heels?

   b. Because Jenna needed additional money, she **augmented** her income by typing term papers for college students.

4 **dispel**
(di-spel')
-verb

   a. Vickie's note of apology was enough to **dispel** the slight anger Rex still felt toward her.

   b. I tried to **dispel** my friend's fears about her blind date that evening by telling her that my parents met on a blind date.

5 **explicit**
(eks-plis'-it)
-adjective

   a. The novel's sex scene was **explicit**, leaving nothing to the imagination.

   b. My parents were very **explicit** about what I could and could not do during their three-day absence. They presented me with a detailed list!

6 **longevity**
(lon-jev'-i-tē)
-noun

   a. Volvos and Hondas are known for their **longevity**, outlasting more expensive cars.

   b. The animal with the greatest **longevity** is the giant land tortoise, which can live several hundred years.

7 **magnitude**
(mag'-nə-tōod')
-noun

   a. Numbers in the millions and billions are of too great a **magnitude** for most people to grasp.

   b. The murder case took on added **magnitude** when it was learned that the dead woman had been the mayor's mistress.

8 **render**
(ren'-dər)
-verb

   a. Don't let the baby near your term paper with that crayon, or she will **render** it unreadable.

   b. Phyllis added so much red pepper to the chili that she **rendered** it too hot to eat.

Matching Words and Definitions

Check your understanding of the eight words by matching each word with its definition. Look back at the sentences in "Eight Words in Context" as needed to decide on the meaning of each word.

_____ 1. **aloof**	a. to drive away as if by scattering; cause to vanish
_____ 2. **ambivalent**	b. size; importance
_____ 3. **augment**	c. stated or shown clearly and exactly
_____ 4. **dispel**	d. having conflicting feelings about someone or something
_____ 5. **explicit**	e. to cause (something) to become; make
_____ 6. **longevity**	f. cool and reserved; distant in personal relations
_____ 7. **magnitude**	g. to increase; make greater, as in strength or quantity
_____ 8. **render**	h. a long span of life; length of life

CAUTION: Do not go any further until you are sure the above answers are correct. If you have studied the "Eight Words in Context," you will know how to match each word. Then you can use the matches to help you in the following practices. Your goal is to reach a point where you don't need to check definitions at all.

➤ Sentence Check 1

Complete each sentence below with the most suitable word from the box. Use each word once.

aloof	ambivalent	augment	dispel
explicit	longevity	magnitude	render

1. The architect decided to add another pillar to the huge building to _____ its support.

2. "Russell seems _____ toward me," Janice said, "as if he both likes and dislikes me."

3. Recent research suggests that our parents' _____ doesn't necessarily affect how long we will live.

4. When I'm frightened, I try to appear _____, since looking cool and distant helps me feel in control.

5. "If you keep walking on the backs of your shoes like that, you will _____ them as flat as the floor," Annie's mother said.

6. If Claude proposes marriage to Jean, he will _____ any doubts she may still have as to whether or not he really loves her.

7. "I try to make my test questions as _____ as possible," said Mr. Baines, "so that my students will know exactly what answers I'm looking for."

8. I began to realize the _____ of the insect population when I read that there are more kinds of insects living today than all other kinds of animals in the world.

Now check your answers to these questions by turning to page 119. Going over the answers carefully will help you prepare for the next two checks, for which answers are not given.

➤ Sentence Check 2

Complete each sentence below with two words from the box. Use each word once.

aloof	ambivalent	augment	dispel
explicit	longevity	magnitude	render

1-2. "Drop dead" seems a pretty _____ way to wish someone reduced _____, but theater people use the expression to mean "Good luck."

3-4. Eye strain from staring at a computer screen _____(e)d the _____ of Harriet's already severe headache.

5-6. I'm _____ about playing with our rock band. I love the music we play, but I'm afraid it will _____ me deaf one of these days.

7-8. Gail is _____ only toward people whom she strongly dislikes. With all others, she soon _____s any feelings of shyness or distrust with her naturally warm and open manner.

➤ Final Check: My Sister's Date

Here is a final opportunity for you to strengthen your knowledge of the eight words. First read the following passage carefully. Then fill in each blank with a word from the box at the top of this page. (Context clues will help you figure out which word goes in which blank.) Use each word once.

I watched as my older sister, Ruth, removed the last spiked curler from her hair. We stared at the result. She somehow had (1)_____(e)d her hair limp as spaghetti. When Ruth started to cry, I comforted her with my usual gentleness: "Why are you such a crybaby about some stupid guy?"

The guy was Steven Meyer. He and Ruth were going to a high school dance. She'd had a crush on him for years, for reasons that escaped me. (I never had figured out what she saw in him.)

When Ruth began to apply her makeup, she gave a terrifying scream that probably reduced my (2)_____ by at least a year. She informed me between sobs that a pimple that made her "look like a witch" had just appeared on her nose. I studied her face, expecting a pimple of truly amazing (3)_____. Instead, I spotted a tiny speck. Again I tried to (4)_____ Ruth's worries. "So, it makes you look like a witch. Don't you want to look bewitching?" But this only seemed to (5)_____ her grief, and she wept again. I took this opportunity to go downstairs and wait for Steven Meyer.

He arrived a half hour before Ruth was ready. Observing him through my thick glasses, I tried to figure out exactly what Ruth saw in him. We talked until she appeared at the top of the stairs. Trying to look (6)_____, she came down very slowly, wearing a cool, distant expression.

When Ruth returned home later that night, her comment about the kind of time she'd had was brief and (7)_____: "Totally rotten." It seemed to me as if Ruth had bypassed feeling (8)_____ about Steven and gone straight from love to hate.

It's just as well, since I've been married to Steven for ten years now.

SCORES: Sentence Check 2 _____ %   Final Check _____ %
Enter your scores above and in the vocabulary performance chart on the inside back cover of the book.

Number right: 8 = 100%   7 = 88%   6 = 75%   5 = 63%   4 = 50%   3 = 38%   2 = 25%   1 = 13%

UNIT FOUR: Test 1

PART A
Choose the word that best completes each sentence and write it in the space provided.

1. **inhibitions**
   habitats
   precedents
   esteems

   Endangered species won't survive unless their _____ are

   preserved.

2. **explicit**
   transient
   fallible
   punitive

   Peter hasn't been _____ about quitting his job, but he's

   hinted at it.

3. **longevity**
   habitat
   inhibition
   precedent

   I didn't let the kids stay up late last night because I didn't want to set a(n)

   _____ for future nights.

4. **punitive**
   vindictive
   implicit
   aloof

   When my brother complained of a shortage of cash, his

   _____ message was "Can you lend me some money?"

5. **feigned**
   rendered
   dwindled
   condoned

   Sandy has _____ her son's temper tantrums for so long that

   he thinks they're acceptable behavior.

6. **esteem**
   longevity
   legacy
   magnitude

   The poker gang laughed when Mom asked to join their game, but their

   _____ rose as she won the first four hands.

7. **ruptured**
   gaped
   formulated
   saturated

   While driving home three hours after her curfew, Lucille

   _____ an excuse she hoped her parents would believe.

8. **exhaustive**
   furtive
   implicit
   vindictive

   After a(n) _____ search during which I crawled around my

   entire apartment, my "missing" contact lens fell out of my eye.

9. **exhaustive**
   ironic
   furtive
   pragmatic

   When Cindy saw Grant's crumpled fender, she made the _____

   comment, "I really like how you've customized your car, Grant."

10. **dwindle**
    feign
    constrict
    pacify

    I accidentally learned about my surprise party, so I had to _____

    surprise when my friends jumped out yelling, "Happy birthday!"

(Continues on next page)

PART B

Circle **C** if the italicized word is used **correctly**. Circle **I** if the word is used **incorrectly.**

C   I   11.   *Saturate* the washcloth by wringing it out.

C   I   12.   Eating dried fruits can be as *detrimental* to your teeth as eating candy.

C   I   13.   Female elephants join together to help each other *nurture* their young.

C   I   14.   In a surprisingly *punitive* mood, our boss let everyone off early last Friday.

C   I   15.   The suspect had such a *furtive* expression that he appeared to be hiding something.

C   I   16.   Mort's back talk *pacified* his father, who then denied him the use of the car for a month.

C   I   17.   After running over a sharp rock, our tire *ruptured*. Luckily, we had a spare in the trunk.

C   I   18.   My grandfather's *pathetic* gardening won him two first prizes in the state flower show.

C   I   19.   I have to ignore Jesse completely now to *dispel* any idea he may have that I'm romantically interested in him.

C   I   20.   In the package, panty hose look so small that it's hard to believe they'll *constrict* enough to fit over a woman's legs.

SCORE: (Number correct) _____ x 5 = _____ %

Enter your scores above and in the vocabulary performance chart on the inside back cover of the book.

UNIT FOUR: Test 2

PART A
Complete each sentence with a word from the box. Use each word once.

aloof	ambivalent	contemplate	fallible	inhibition
legacy	magnitude	muted	reconcile	render

1. To make the bright green a more _____ shade, the painter added gray.

2. Cooking vegetables for too long _____s them less nutritious.

3. Inez may seem _____, but she's not cold once she gets to know you.

4. Why _____ dropping out of school when you've got only two semesters to go?

5. Mack has _____ feelings about his job. He loves the work but hates his boss.

6. No one realized the _____ of our grandmother's depression until she tried to kill herself.

7. My love of the outdoors is a(n) _____ from my grandfather, who often hiked in the mountains.

8. At first, Tiffany was somewhat reluctant to sit in Santa Claus' lap, but she overcame her

    _____ when she saw that he was handing out candy canes.

9. As the wedding drew near, Brenda had to _____ herself to the fact that her son would marry a woman she disliked.

10. To remind everyone that we're all _____, my boss keeps a giant eraser on his desk imprinted with the words "For Big Mistakes."

(Continues on next page)

PART B
Circle **C** if the italicized word is used **correctly**. Circle **I** if the word is used **incorrectly**.

C   I   11.   Karen found the chicken salad *vile*. One small taste made her gag.

C   I   12.   I asked Sal to *augment* the stereo because it was giving me a headache.

C   I   13.   Some spiders have surprising *longevity*, living as long as twenty years.

C   I   14.   The Daniels' *transient* marriage has already lasted over fifty years.

C   I   15.   When the *vindictive* tenant was evicted, he broke all the windows in his apartment.

C   I   16.   Being a *pragmatic* person, my brother values music and poetry more than practical things.

C   I   17.   An *avid* reader, Judy spends much of her time enjoying newspapers, magazines and books.

C   I   18.   My liking for my supervisor *dwindled* as his temper grew shorter and his list of "do not's" grew longer.

C   I   19.   Interested in the cartoon on TV, the little boy just *gaped* casually at his mother as she left for work.

C   I   20.   If a flamingo is *deficient* in a type of vitamin A, its feathers won't turn pink.

SCORE: (Number correct) _____ x 5 = _____ %

Enter your scores above and in the vocabulary performance chart on the inside back cover of the book.

UNIT FOUR: Test 3

PART A: Synonyms

In the space provided, write the letter of the choice that is most nearly the **same** in meaning as the boldfaced word.

_____ 1. **saturate**   a) burst   b) make   c) soak   d) scatter

_____ 2. **gape**   a) look for   b) notice   c) see   d) stare

_____ 3. **condone**   a) forbid   b) put up with   c) encourage   d) imitate

_____ 4. **vindictive**   a) practical   b) complete   c) vengeful   d) surprising

_____ 5. **contemplate**   a) think about   b) decide   c) prefer   d) wait

_____ 6. **ambivalent**   a) active   b) sure   c) not harmful   d) having mixed feelings

_____ 7. **esteem**   a) curiosity   b) disapproval   c) acceptance   d) respect

_____ 8. **legacy**   a) promise   b) example   c) inheritance   d) increase

_____ 9. **feign**   a) pretend   b) conceal   c) develop   d) oppose

_____ 10. **habitat**   a) hobby   b) environment   c) lifestyle   d) diet

_____ 11. **longevity**   a) youth   b) good health   c) life span   d) death

_____ 12. **pacify**   a) care for   b) encourage   c) admire   d) calm down

_____ 13. **formulate**   a) recognize   b) aim for   c) develop   d) promote

_____ 14. **rupture**   a) accept   b) draw forth   c) burst   d) fill as much as possible

_____ 15. **implicit**   a) suggested   b) in conflict   c) devoted   d) brief

_____ 16. **precedent**   a) effect   b) earlier example   c) goal   d) main cause

_____ 17. **dispel**   a) recognize   b) oppose   c) drive away   d) create

_____ 18. **inhibition**   a) something handed down   b) holding back   c) tone   d) wish

_____ 19. **magnitude**   a) favorable opinion   b) length of life   c) location   d) importance

_____ 20. **render**   a) scatter   b) cause to become   c) increase   d) make narrower

(Continues on next page)

113

PART B: Antonyms
In the space provided, write the letter of the choice that is most nearly the **opposite** in meaning to the boldfaced word.

_____21. **pragmatic**   **a)** mistaken   **b)** impractical   **c)** offensive   **d)** untalented

_____22. **aloof**   **a)** friendly   **b)** mean   **c)** handsome   **d)** ambitious

_____23. **constrict**   **a)** admire   **b)** build   **c)** accept   **d)** make wider

_____24. **pathetic**   **a)** admirable   **b)** possible   **c)** broad   **d)** safe

_____25. **avid**   **a)** quiet   **b)** rare   **c)** unenthusiastic   **d)** impractical

_____26. **detrimental**   **a)** pleasant   **b)** helpful   **c)** respectful   **d)** clear

_____27. **augment**   **a)** decrease   **b)** oppose   **c)** deny   **d)** avoid

_____28. **furtive**   **a)** wise   **b)** successful   **c)** unhidden   **d)** impossible

_____29. **muted**   **a)** brightened   **b)** corrected   **c)** forbidden   **d)** out in the open

_____30. **deficient**   **a)** kind   **b)** sufficient   **c)** useful   **d)** permanent

_____31. **punitive**   **a)** in favor of   **b)** organized   **c)** straightforward   **d)** rewarding

_____32. **transient**   **a)** frequent   **b)** permanent   **c)** rare   **d)** possible

_____33. **dwindle**   **a)** replace   **b)** increase   **c)** reveal   **d)** improve

_____34. **exhaustive**   **a)** poorly stated   **b)** boring   **c)** impractical   **d)** incomplete

_____35. **reconcile**   **a)** contrast   **b)** accept   **c)** cause to vanish   **d)** decide to reject

_____36. **nurture**   **a)** dislike   **b)** win   **c)** neglect   **d)** fail to notice

_____37. **fallible**   **a)** perfect   **b)** beautiful   **c)** understandable   **d)** willing

_____38. **explicit**   **a)** poorly supported   **b)** lengthy   **c)** vague   **d)** complicated

_____39. **ironic**   **a)** strong   **b)** expected   **c)** true   **d)** covering few details

_____40. **vile**   **a)** organized   **b)** permanent   **c)** large   **d)** pleasant

---

SCORE: (Number correct) _____ x 2.5 = _____ %

Enter your scores above and in the vocabulary performance chart on the inside back cover of the book.

UNIT FOUR: Test 4

PART A
Complete each sentence in a way that clearly shows you understand the meaning of the boldfaced word. Take a minute to plan your answer before you write.

Example: To increase your **longevity**, *exercise frequently and avoid tobacco, alcohol, and high-fat foods.*

1. Ramona, who is **pragmatic**, spends her money on such things as _____

   _____

2. One thing the nursery-school teacher did to **nurture** each child each day was _____

   _____

3. The critic summed up how **pathetic** the actor's performance was with this comment: " _____

   _____

4. The car accident **rendered** Philip _____

   _____

5. A student **deficient** in study skills might _____

   _____

6. The **magnitude** of Carol's musical talent became clear when _____

   _____

7. Just how **fallible** the house builder was could be seen by _____

   _____

8. I have had to **reconcile** myself to the fact that _____

   _____

9. When he wasn't invited to the wedding, the bride's **vindictive** cousin _____

   _____

10. I'm such an **avid** fan of _____ that I'll _____

   _____

(Continues on next page)

PART B

After each boldfaced word are a *synonym* (a word that means the same as the boldfaced word), an *antonym* (a word that means the opposite of the boldfaced word), and a word that is neither. Mark the synonym with an *S* and the antonym with an *A*.

	Example: **dwindle**	_S_ lessen	_A_ increase	_____ turn
11-12.	**aloof**	_____ angry	_____ friendly	_____ reserved
13-14.	**detrimental**	_____ harmful	_____ organized	_____ beneficial
15-16.	**punitive**	_____ rewarding	_____ requiring	_____ punishing
17-18.	**transient**	_____ brief	_____ permanent	_____ lively
19-20.	**explicit**	_____ vague	_____ loud	_____ clear

PART C

Use five of the following ten words in sentences. Make it clear that you know the meaning of the word you use. Feel free to use the past tense or plural form of a word.

condone	contemplate	esteem	feign	furtive
gape	habitat	inhibition	pacify	vile

21. _____

_____

22. _____

_____

23. _____

_____

24. _____

_____

25. _____

SCORE: (Number correct) _____ x 4 = _____ %

Enter your scores above and in the vocabulary performance chart on the inside back cover of the book.

A. Limited Answer Key

An Important Note: Be sure to use this answer key as a learning tool only. You should not turn to this key until you have considered carefully the sentence in which a given word appears.

Used properly, the key will help you to learn words and to prepare for the activities and tests for which answers are not given. For ease of reference, the title of the "Final Check" passage in each chapter appears in parentheses.

Chapter 1 (Joseph Palmer)

Previewing the Words

1. antagonist
2. amoral
3. malign
4. encounter
5. absolve
6. adamant
7. animosity
8. eccentric

Sentence Check 1

1. adamant
2. encounter
3. malign
4. amoral
5. absolve
6. antagonist
7. animosity
8. eccentric

Chapter 2 (A Cruel Sport)

Previewing the Words

1. obsolete
2. tangible
3. engross
4. elicit
5. escalate
6. acclaim
7. terminate
8. exploit

Sentence Check 1

1. tangible
2. obsolete
3. acclaim
4. escalate
5. engross
6. exploit
7. terminate
8. elicit

Chapter 3 (No Luck with Women)

Previewing the Words

1. assail
2. allusion
3. euphemism
4. altruistic
5. arbitrary
6. banal
7. mercenary
8. appease

Sentence Check 1

1. mercenary
2. allusion
3. altruistic
4. assail
5. euphemism
6. appease
7. arbitrary
8. banal

Chapter 4 (Accident and Recovery)

Previewing the Words

1. persevere
2. venture
3. fluctuate
4. rehabilitate
5. calamity
6. comprehensive
7. turmoil
8. ponder

Sentence Check 1

1. calamity
2. ponder
3. comprehensive
4. persevere
5. rehabilitate
6. turmoil
7. fluctuate
8. venture

Chapter 5 (Animal Senses)

Previewing the Words

1. mobile
2. discern
3. orient
4. attribute
5. exemplify
6. enhance
7. nocturnal
8. attest

Sentence Check 1

1. enhance
2. attest
3. exemplify
4. nocturnal
5. discern
6. orient
7. mobile
8. attribute

Chapter 6 (Money Problems)

Previewing the Words

1. constitute
2. nominal
3. prerequisite
4. decipher
5. default
6. predominant
7. concurrent
8. confiscate

Sentence Check 1

1. predominant
2. concurrent
3. constitute
4. prerequisite
5. nominal
6. decipher
7. default
8. confiscate

Chapter 7 (The New French Employee)

Previewing the Words

1. degenerate
2. vulnerable
3. implausible
4. sinister
5. suffice
6. incoherent
7. sanctuary
8. intricate

Sentence Check 1

1. suffice
2. sinister
3. vulnerable
4. intricate
5. implausible
6. sanctuary
7. incoherent
8. degenerate

Chapter 8 (A Cruel Teacher)

Previewing the Words

1. blight
2. immaculate
3. qualm
4. garble
5. blatant
6. retaliate
7. gloat
8. plagiarism

Sentence Check 1

1. immaculate
2. blight
3. gloat
4. blatant
5. garble
6. retaliate
7. qualm
8. plagiarism

Chapter 9 (Learning to Study)

Previewing the Words

1. intermittent
2. curtail
3. incentive
4. devastate
5. indispensable
6. succumb
7. incorporate
8. digress

Sentence Check 1

1. Intermittent
2. devastate
3. incorporate
4. indispensable
5. incentive
6. curtail
7. digress
8. succumb

Chapter 10 (The Mad Monk)

Previewing the Words

1. alleviate
2. intrinsic
3. benefactor
4. revulsion
5. infamous
6. speculate
7. virile
8. covert

Sentence Check 1

1. intrinsic
2. alleviate
3. virile
4. infamous
5. covert
6. revulsion
7. speculate
8. benefactor

Chapter 11 (Conflict over Holidays)

Previewing the Words

1. agnostic
2. lucrative
3. abstain
4. aspire
5. mandatory
6. dissent
7. deficit
8. benevolent

Sentence Check 1

1. aspire
2. benevolent
3. mandatory
4. abstain
5. deficit
6. dissent
7. agnostic
8. lucrative

Chapter 12 (Dr. Martin Luther King, Jr.)

Previewing the Words

1. prevalent
2. contemporary
3. quest
4. Conversely
5. charisma
6. traumatic
7. proponent
8. extrovert

Sentence Check 1

1. Conversely
2. extrovert
3. prevalent
4. proponent
5. charisma
6. contemporary
7. traumatic
8. quest

Chapter 13 (Relating to Parents)

Previewing the Words

1. prone
2. congenial
3. impasse
4. rationale
5. perception
6. prompt
7. flippant
8. rapport

Sentence Check 1

1. prone
2. congenial
3. flippant
4. prompt
5. rapport
6. impasse
7. perception
8. rationale

Chapter 14 (The Nightmare of Gym)

Previewing the Words

1. divulge
2. detract
3. elation
4. expulsion
5. averse
6. nullify
7. endow
8. ominous

Sentence Check 1

1. detract
2. averse
3. elation
4. nullified
5. endow
6. expulsion
7. ominous
8. divulge

Chapter 15 (A Model Teacher)

Previewing the Words

1. diligent
2. transcend
3. consensus
4. niche
5. deplete
6. empathy
7. waive
8. complacent

Sentence Check 1

1. waive
2. deplete
3. transcend
4. complacent
5. niche
6. diligent
7. consensus
8. empathy

Chapter 16 (Shoplifter)

Previewing the Words

1. gape
2. furtive
3. punitive
4. contemplate
5. feign
6. condone
7. pathetic
8. precedent

Sentence Check 1

1. gape
2. contemplate
3. precedent
4. condone
5. furtive
6. pathetic
7. feign
8. punitive

Chapter 17 (A Nutty Newspaper Office)

Previewing the Words

1. implicit
2. saturate
3. ironic
4. inhibition
5. detrimental
6. deficient
7. rupture
8. vindictive

Sentence Check 1

1. deficient
2. rupture
3. ironic
4. detrimental
5. inhibition
6. vindictive
7. saturate
8. implicit

Chapter 18 (Roughing It)

Previewing the Words

1. constrict
2. formulate
3. fallible
4. habitat
5. reconcile
6. vile
7. exhaustive
8. pragmatic

Sentence Check 1

1. vile
2. reconcile
3. constrict
4. formulate
5. exhaustive
6. habitat
7. pragmatic
8. fallible

Chapter 19 (Getting Scared)

Previewing the Words

1. transient
2. dwindle
3. esteem
4. muted
5. pacify
6. avid
7. nurture
8. legacy

Sentence Check 1

1. nurture
2. dwindle
3. muted
4. pacify
5. transient
6. esteem
7. avid
8. legacy

Chapter 20 (My Sister's Date)

Previewing the Words

1. longevity
2. magnitude
3. ambivalent
4. aloof
5. augment
6. explicit
7. dispel
8. render

Sentence Check 1

1. augment
2. ambivalent
3. longevity
4. aloof
5. render
6. dispel
7. explicit
8. magnitude

B. *Dictionary Use*

It isn't always possible to figure out the meaning of a word from its context, and that's where a dictionary comes in. Following is some basic information to help you use a dictionary.

HOW TO FIND A WORD

A dictionary contains so many words that it can take a while to find the one you're looking for. But if you know how to use guide words, you can find a word rather quickly. *Guide words* are the two words at the top of each dictionary page. The first guide word tells what the first word is on the page. The second guide word tells what the last word is on that page. The other words on a page fall alphabetically between the two guide words. So when you look up a word, find the two guide words that alphabetically surround the word you're looking for.

• Which of the following pair of guide words would be on a page with the word *heckle*?

    heaven/heel   **headache/hearing**   **helmet/henpeck**

The answer to this question and the ones that follow are given on the next page.

HOW TO USE A DICTIONARY LISTING

A dictionary listing includes many pieces of information. For example, here is a listing from the *Random House College Dictionary*, Paperback Edition. Note that it includes much more than just a definition.

    driz·zle (driz'əl), *v.*, **-zled, -zling,** *n.* —*v.* **1.** to rain gently and steadily in fine drops.
    — *n.* **2.** a very light rain. —**driz'zly,** *adj.*

Key parts of a dictionary entry are listed and explained below.

Syllables. Dots separate dictionary entry words into syllables. Note that *drizzle* has one dot, which breaks the word into two syllables.

• To practice seeing the syllable breakdown in a dictionary entry, write the number of syllables in each word below.

    re·quire _____   **de·ci·sive** _____   **mel·o·dra·ma** _____

Pronunciation guide. The information within parentheses after the entry word shows how to pronounce the entry word. This pronunciation guide includes two types of symbols: pronunciation symbols and accent marks.

Pronunciation symbols represent the consonant and vowel sounds in a word. The consonant sounds are probably very familiar to you, but you may find it helpful to review some of the sounds of the vowels—*a, e, i, o,* and *u.* Every dictionary has a key explaining the sounds of its pronunciation symbols, including the long and short sounds of vowels.

Long vowels have the sound of their own names. For example, the *a* in *pay* and the *o* in *no* both have long vowel sounds. Long vowel sounds are shown by a line above the vowel.

In the *Random House College Dictionary,* the *short vowels* are shown by the use of the vowel itself, with no other markings. Thus the *i* in the first syllable of *drizzle* is a short *i.* What do the short vowels sound like? Below are words from the *RHCD* pronunciation key which illustrate the *short vowel* sounds.

    a bat   **e** set   **i** big   **o** box   **u** up

This key means, for example, that the *a* in *bat* has the short-*a* sound.

• Which of the words below has a short vowel sound? Which has a long vowel sound?

trick _____   **scene** _____   **pest** _____

Another pronunciation symbol is the *schwa*, which looks like an upside-down *e*. It stands for certain rapidly spoken, unaccented vowel sounds, such as the *a* in *above*, the *e* in *item*, the *i* in *easily*, the *o* in *gallop*, and the *u* in *circus*. Here are three words that include the schwa sound:

mus·cle (mus'əl)   **boul·der** (bōl'dər)   **ren·o·vate** (ren'ə-vāt')

• Which syllable in *drizzle* contains the schwa sound, the first or the second? _____

Accent marks are small black marks that tell you which syllable to emphasize, or stress, as you say a word. An accent mark follows *driz* in the pronunciation guide for *drizzle*, which tells you to stress the first syllable of *drizzle*. Syllables with no accent mark are not stressed. Some syllables are in between, and they are marked with a lighter accent mark.

• Which syllable has the stronger accent in *penicillin*? _____

pen·i·cil·lin (pen'i-sil'in)

Parts of Speech. After the pronunciation key and before each set of definitions, the entry word's parts of speech are given. The parts of speech are abbreviated as follows:

noun—*n.*   pronoun—*pron.*   adjective—*adj.*   adverb—*adv.*   verb—*v.*

• The listing for *drizzle* shows it has two parts of speech. Write them below:

_____   _____

Definitions. Words often have more than one meaning. When they do, each meaning is usually numbered in the dictionary. You can tell which definition of a word fits a given sentence by the meaning of the sentence. For example, the word *finish* has several definitions, including these two: **1.** the final part or conclusion. **2.** surface texture.

• Show with a check which definition applies in each sentence below:

The runner collapsed at the finish of the race.   1 ___   2 ___

That table has a finish as smooth as glass.   1 ___   2 ___

Other Information. After the definitions in a listing in a hardbound dictionary, you may get information about the *origin* of a word. Such information about origins, also known as *etymology*, is usually given in brackets. And you may sometimes be given one or more synonyms or antonyms for the entry word. *Synonyms* are words that are similar in meaning to the entry word; *antonyms* are words that are opposite in meaning.

WHICH DICTIONARIES TO OWN

You will find it useful to own two recent dictionaries: a small paperback dictionary to carry to class and a hardbound dictionary, which contains more information than a small paperback one. Among the good dictionaries strongly recommended are both the paperback and hardcover editions of the following:

The Random House College Dictionary
The American Heritage Dictionary
Webster's New World Dictionary

ANSWERS TO THE DICTIONARY QUESTIONS

Guide words: *heaven/heel*
Number of syllables: 2, 3, 4
Vowels: *trick, pest* (short); *scene* (long)
Schwa: second syllable of *drizzle*

Accent: stronger accent on third syllable
Parts of speech: noun and verb
Definitions: 1; 2

C. Word List

absolve, 5
abstain, 61
acclaim, 9
adamant, 5
agnostic, 61
alleviate, 49
allusion, 13
aloof, 105
altruistic, 13
ambivalent, 105
amoral, 5
animosity, 5
antagonist, 5
appease, 13
arbitrary, 13
aspire, 61
assail, 13
attest, 21
attribute, 21
augment, 105
averse, 73
avid, 101
banal, 13
benefactor, 49
benevolent, 61
blatant, 41
blight, 41
calamity, 17
charisma, 65
complacent, 77
comprehensive, 17
concurrent, 33
condone, 89
confiscate, 33
congenial, 69
consensus, 77
constitute, 33
constrict, 97
contemplate, 89
contemporary, 65
conversely, 65
covert, 49
curtail, 45
decipher, 33
default, 33

deficient, 93
deficit, 61
degenerate, 37
deplete, 77
detract, 73
detrimental, 93
devastate, 45
digress, 45
diligent, 77
discern, 21
dispel, 105
dissent, 61
divulge, 73
dwindle, 101
eccentric, 5
elation, 73
elicit, 9
empathy, 77
encounter, 5
endow, 73
engross, 9
enhance, 21
escalate, 9 ·
esteem, 101
euphemism, 13
exemplify, 21
exhaustive, 97
explicit, 105
exploit, 9
expulsion, 73
extrovert, 65
fallible, 97
feign, 89
flippant, 69
fluctuate, 17
formulate, 97
furtive, 89
gape, 89
garble, 41
gloat, 41
habitat, 97
immaculate, 41
impasse, 69
implausible, 37
implicit, 93

incentive, 45
incoherent, 37
incorporate, 45
indispensable, 45
infamous, 49
inhibition, 93
intermittent, 45
intricate, 37
intrinsic, 49
ironic, 93
legacy, 101
longevity, 105
lucrative, 61
magnitude, 105
malign, 5
mandatory, 61
mercenary, 13
mobile, 21
muted, 101
niche, 77
nocturnal, 21
nominal, 33
nullify, 73
nurture, 101
obsolete, 9
ominous
orient, 21
pacify, 101
pathetic, 89
perception, 69
persevere, 17
plagiarism, 41
ponder, 17
pragmatic, 97
precedent, 89
predominant, 33
prerequisite, 33
prevalent, 65
prompt, 69
prone, 69
proponent, 65
punitive, 89
qualm, 41
quest, 65
rapport, 69

rationale, 69
reconcile, 97
rehabilitate, 17
render, 105
retaliate, 41
revulsion, 49
rupture, 93
sanctuary, 37
saturate, 93
sinister, 37
speculate, 49
succumb, 45
suffice, 37
tangible, 9
terminate, 9
transcend, 77
transient, 101
traumatic, 65
turmoil, 17
venture, 17
vile, 97
vindictive, 93
virile, 49
vulnerable, 37
waive, 77